CW00739649

Fantastic Feet

a fascinating insight to foot and hand reading

Feet are a window in to what may
really be going on

A simple and easy illustrated guide

Special Thanks

To everyone who had requested this book and nudged me into action!

To everyone who loves people and their feet, for showing me the wonders of their stories.

To my family and friends for their love, encouragement and support.

Jayne Thompson (Barny Books)   Cathy Brown
Dave Ricks (Dave Ricks Web & Design) Deborah Hitt
Jim McEwen (Crayfish Design)   Anne Coles
Helen Peberdy   Ruth Bateman
Lousia Gard   Kate David

About the Author

Sue Ricks is an inspirational teacher and practitioner of Complementary Therapies. She has run a successful training school and Clinic in the midlands (UK) for over 25 years.

Sue has been awarded an Honorary Membership of the Association of Reflexologist (HMAR) and was the principal lead lecturer in Reflexology at The University of Derby. Sue has lectured in the UK, Ireland, Europe & The United States. Sue has presented on BBC TV, ITV, BBC Radio Nottingham & Leicester and other radio stations.

Sue provides training in Gentle Touch™ Reflexology, Reflexology for Babies & Children, advanced reflexology skills, other therapies, plus treatments. Sue has also produced other Books and DVD's.

Introduction

The First Steps to Foot Reading

The Basics

Getting Started

Section One

The Grid System – A Guide to Reading The Zones

Section Two

Colours – Understanding the Colours Seen and Their Relevance

Section Three

Shape Of The Feet – An Insight Into The Shape of the Feet and Toes

Review

Benefitting Everyone

Contents

Introduction – The First Steps to Foot Reading

What Will I Get From this Guide?	6
Sign Posting for This Foot Reading Guide	7
Foot Reading – Fact or Fiction?	8
Best Foot Forward	9
The Building Blocks	10
Feet Versus Hands	10
Changing Times	10

The Basics – Getting Started

Getting Started	12
A Person and Their Feet	13
You and Your Feet	15
The Actor and the Actress	17
Foot Reading in Action	18
Privacy and Disclosure	21

Section One – The Grid System

The Grid System	25
Vertical Grid	25
The Other Foot!	29
Hands Too	31
Horizontal Grid	33
Full Grid	39
Double Sectors	41
Dual Theme Sectors	43
Sector Meanings	46
'Thoughts' Means	46
'Feelings' Means	46
'Creativity and Doings' Means	46
'Communication' Means	47
'Family and Security' Means	47

Section Two – Colours

Hand and Feet Colours	50
Colour Chart	53
Red – (Anger or Embarrassment)	55
Yellow – (Fed Up)	57
Orange – (Frustrated or Annoyed)	59
Blue – (Hurt)	61
Black / Grey - (Extreme Hurt)	63
Brown – (Browned Off, Exceptionally Fed Up)	65
Green – (Envy or Jealousy)	67
Purple – (Bruised Emotions)	69
White – (Washed Out / Exhausted)	71
Natural Colour / Pink – Happy and Healthy	73
Colours and Observations	75
Depth of Colour	75
Repeated Colours	75
Colour Change in Action	76

Section Three – Shape of the Feet

Right Foot and Left Foot	81
Size of Feet	83
Big Feet	83
Small Feet	85
Shape of Feet	85
Narrow Feet	85
Broad (Wide) Foot	87
Angled Feet	89
Soles Facing Each Other	90
Walking on Ball of the Foot – Tip Toes	90
Flat Footed	90
Walking on the Outside of Their Feet	91
Floppy Feet	91
Rigid Feet	92
Ticklish Feet	93
Temperature	94
Foot Condition	95
Cracked Heels	95
Bunions	99
Swollen Feet – Oedema	102
Toe Reading	105
Toes	107
Straight Toes	107
Crossed Toes	107
Length of Toes	109
Prominent Toes – Noticeably Longer	109
Shorter toes	109
Large, Long, Wide Big Toe (Hallux)	110
Longer Second Toe	115
Longer Third Toe	115
Long Fourth Toe	117
Long Fifth (Little) Toe	117
Little Toe	119
Long Toe Stems	122
Wide – Strong Toes	123
Long and Wide Toes	123
Nails	125
Ingrowing Toe Nails	125
No Nails	125
Nail Fungal Infections	127
Finger Nail Biting	127

Review – Benefiting Everyone

Self Care	129
What to Say and What Not to Say	130
Self Reflection	133
This Book	134
Grid Example	137
Examples	138
A Carer's Feet	139
Charts	140

Introduction

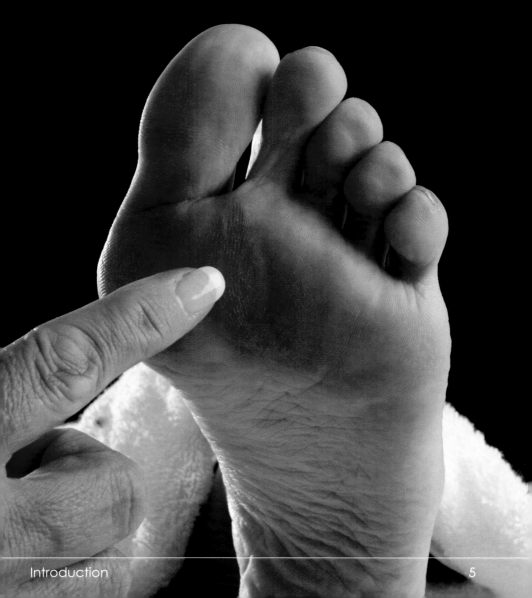

What Will I Get From This Guide?

- An awareness of how useful foot reading can be

- An opportunity to discover the depth of Foot Reading

- Find out what may be going on with someone without them needing to tell you

- Find out more about yourself

- Identify when others are in need

- Discover when you may benefit from more knowledge, help or support

- Understand your clients, family and friends more

- Gain more information about what others may be feeling and experiencing

- Learn about others preferences and so be able to work more effectively with them

- Be a more understanding partner, parent or carer

Sign Posting for This Foot Reading Guide

This guide is created in three sections to allow an easy passage through the content.

You can take it at your own pace and either read it through from beginning to end or you may choose to dip in and out according to your specific query or area of interest.

Section One will give the basic foot reading grids and how it relates to hand too.

Section Two provides information on the meanings of colours found in or on feet.

Section Three describes various foot factors and detailed information about feet, toes, shapes, conditions.

Foot Reading – Fact or Fiction?

This guide has come about as a result of many years of working with people and recognising that there are some amazing insights that can be gleaned by knowing how to read feet.

Foot reading is about knowing more about an individual – their likes, how they work and process information and how well they are (or not) coping with their lives. It is also a great way to self reflect or monitor your own progress in life. In fact, it's an amazing opportunity to enhance one's own self awareness.

Even before my career involved working with people and their feet, I found myself wondering why people's feet were so different. I wondered why some people had hammertoes whilst others had long slender toes. I think I assumed it was caused by the shoes they were wearing or had worn in their earlier years. However, it was only when I began my career as a reflexologist that I realised there is so much more to this fascinating subject of people and their feet.

I began to keep notes and record my findings and started to notice that patterns were emerging. Over time, as I recorded the detail, I realised the accuracy of the findings and the interpretations that related to them. This book describes these findings and interpretations and I hope that you enjoy and use it in the depth that feels right for you.

The aim of this book to help those who are interested to develop another layer of self awareness or appreciation and support of others. Once we know some hidden feeling, emotions or factors that may have limited our potential, we can be more loving and tolerant. It's easy to be more loving when we understand.

It's essential to remember that 'Energy Follows Thought' and what we focus on is increased. So always focus on strength not weaknesses.

Best Foot Forward

Foot Reading can help you to really get to know more about someone.

It can reveal the key factors about people, including:

- Their strengths

- The ways they process information

- What motivates them

- What are some of the factors that are affecting them at the present time

- Their state of mind

- The degree of pressure they are under

- How calm they are

- If they are on the right track

- Their natural qualities

The information is revealed by every aspect of the feet including foot wear, foot shape, toes and even their colour. We can also gain valuable information by noticing if these aspects are present on just one foot or both.

Some people only get problems like blisters, calluses or other characteristics on one foot. In foot reading these can be indicators to aspects of their life and can help us become more aware and understand how life is for them.

There are also indictors on peoples hands. These include observations of any cuts and bruises etc. Although this books focuses mainly on foot reading, the basic principles apply to the hands too.

The Building Blocks

Foot and hand reading can tell you much about an individual's personality; their approach to life, the fundamental issues that underpin their way of life and what is important to them.

We have unique feet in the same way that we have unique fingerprints or iris patterns of the eyes. Although at first glance all feet may appear the same, in actual fact, no two feet are the same.

Our feet and hands reflect us, our journey and individual nature.

Feet Versus Hands

Our feet represent how we stand up to life, while our hands represent how we handle life so it is always interesting to see how people's feet versus hands are. Hand reading is very different to palmistry but is similar to foot reading.

Feet are what you stand for and you stand 'it'.

Hands are what you're handling and how you handle 'it'.

Changing Times

It can be fascinating to see how feet or hands change over time. The feet may stay the same for years before the person's life takes a new direction or has added or reduced responsibilities. When their life changes, their feet change too. Feet mirror the effect of the life change and how the person is affected physically, emotionally or energetically by it.

Our feet and hands show how we are at the time, the reality of now. They can show subtle or significant changes as we adjust when any of our circumstances, emotions or attitude alters.

The Basics

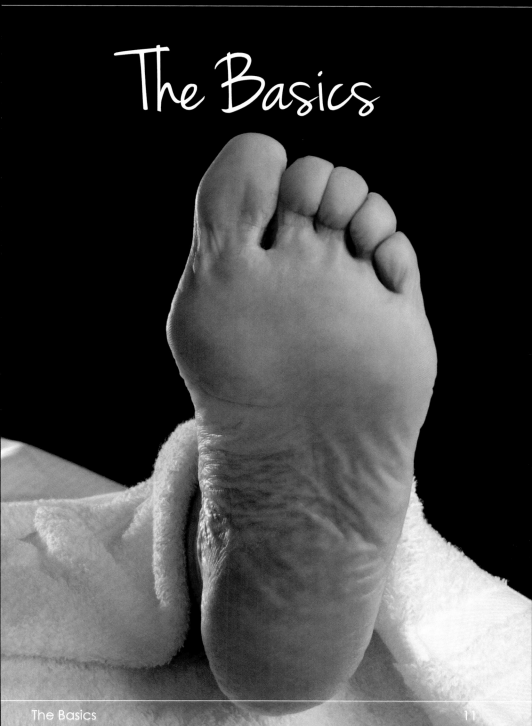

Getting Started

Everyone's foot / feet are unique and individual to them.

They are a variety of:

- Shapes

- Sizes

- Colours

With a range of different:

- Toe positions

- Foot positions

- Feet defects

- Lines and marks

- Bone deformities

- Skin infections

- Scars

- Distinctive appearance

All of these can have additional meanings and relate to an individual and their life.

A Person and Their Feet

There are a large number of things that we can tell by someone's foot or feet. Whilst this is not an exact science, it is incredible how much more information we can glean when we understand some of the indications shown on our feet.

Some of the information that can be obtained is:

- Natural skills, talents and aptitudes

- Where or how a person may be finding life difficult

- Personality traits

- Strengths

- Coping strategies

- Appropriate careers

- How they interpret life

- What are the key aspects of life for them

- How balanced they are

- Potential achieved

- Potential to be realised

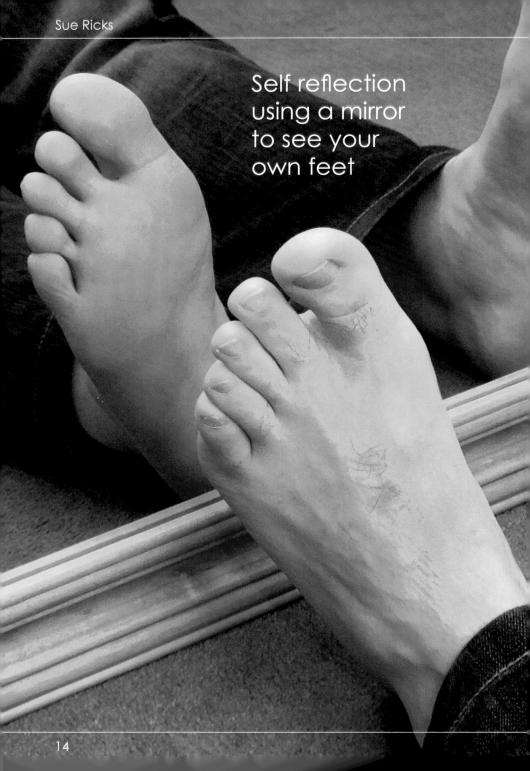

Self reflection
using a mirror
to see your
own feet

You and Your Feet

Luckily enough the person who will benefit the most from reading feet is YOU!

If you want to give yourself and your life a quick appraisal, have a look at your own feet.

Take time to really look and pay attention and become aware of how they look and consider:

- Their colour and where it varies

- The shape of your feet

- The position of your toes

- Are there any imperfections, markings, scars or any other markings?

- Any obvious or subtle changes

You may wish to use this book to assess what you see or you may choose to keep a photograph or sketch of your feet or hands to see how they are changing throughout a period of personal transformation.

The differences can be revealing and can tell you how you are doing. This can be a confirmation of what you already know, or it can be a wake-up call to something that requires your attention.

One of my students started their Gentle Touch™ Reflexology course during a time of great life change and decided to take a photograph of her own feet as a point of reference to review at a later date to see how far they had come. She knew that she would be learning about foot reading and decided to use herself as a test case.

Her initial observation was that she had bright red toes that curled over. Her big toe was quite angled in towards the other toes and the area around her heels was pale and also very cracked.

After most of her substantial life change had taken place, her feet were pinker in colour (less red and angry), her toes had straightened up, plus the skin on her heels had greatly improved.

This showed her to have overcome some of her anger (pink - not red) and have a better ability to become the person that she is (straighter toes). She was more confident, calmer and more comfortable with her way of life. She felt more secure (heels in good order) and able to honour things that were important to her.

The Actor and the Actress

How many people do you know who seem to have their life made? Their life looks as if it flows effortlessly, they are always smiling and seem happy. Maybe they seem confident and can cope with anything. Yet when you really get to know them, it may be surprising that there appears to be so much more going on that you could ever have imagined. All of this can be seen by observing feet and hands.

Many years ago I was with a very laid back friend of mine who I had known for a long time. She was so laid back about everything in her life that she was nearly horizontal! I was amazed when she took her shoes off and relaxed in my recliner chair. I was able to see the 'real' her as revealed by her feet! They clearly showed how stressed she was, how fed up she was with her life and how angry she had become. I was astonished at the difference between the image she was projecting and the battle that she must be going through every day in order to appear so calm.

Over the ensuing years we became even closer and I was privileged to find out more about what was going on behind the scenes. She explained why she battles so hard to appear chilled out and why she did not feel remotely calm! She is now addressing these issues and has also taken great personal pride and pleasure in noticing the changes in her feet as she clears away her emotional baggage.

This made me realise how good we all are at being actors and actresses and can project a very different image to the world to what we feel underneath. Our reality may be very different to the one that we are happy to portray to the world.

Foot Reading in Action

It is wonderful to see either your own feet, or those of others, regain a beautiful natural colour after challenging times. These challenges will also be shown through other colours or hues on the soles of the foot or feet.

Any personal development work or change of circumstances will show as colour and shape changes in our feet. Many find it validating to have something that shows their progress so clearly as ideally, times of challenge are hopefully followed by self awareness, personal growth, love and understanding.

We can record progress and also support ourselves through learning and personal development. Times of peace, acceptance and self care will look very different, on our hands of feet, to times of stress, anxiety or trauma. Simply looking at your feet or hands can sometimes help to steer you in the right direction by highlighting your current strengths and the issues that may be of priority to resolve or seek assistance for.

On many occasions I have seen that the issues that someone is facing may actually be other people's issues that they have taken on as their own.

Foot reading can make it easier to understand what is going on by recognising the potential of the individual and also acknowledging the hidden or concealed factors. It may be obvious on a person's feet that they are screaming inside but are outwardly smiling broadly to the outside world.

One of my students is a nurse and finds that foot reading helps her enormously to assist patients. She may see their feet and recognise how they are feeling. She had one case where a lovely lady was sitting on her bed, smiling and seemed fine. However her feet communicated a different story as they revealed that she was actually very angry, hurt and totally lacking in confidence. The lady appeared serene on the surface but underneath she was clearly really struggling.

The nurse was able to take the time to stop and talk to the lady and get to know her. She found out why the woman was so angry. Apparently she had been dropped off by her family and left to cope alone with her operation and her stay in hospital. This made her feel inwardly angry as she had always given full support to her son and hoped they would have reciprocated by being more supportive. She was terrified that she would have a bad time but did not like to admit it.

The nurse realised that she had only stopped to talk to the lady because she had seen her feet and recognised that her smiling face was not reflecting her authentic feelings. If she had just seen the image that the lady projected of a smiling and content lady she would have walked on by. Luckily the nurse's ability to foot read gave her an added advantage to connect with the patient and be there for her in a very caring and honest way.

Privacy and Disclosure

It is one thing to know and it is another thing to say!

Foot reading is both wonderful and yet also carries a great deal of responsibility with it. We need to be careful what and when, or even *if* we say anything about what we have observed.

People have the right to privacy and may not be aware of what you can tell from their feet.

Their soul is expressed via their sole!

Many people cover their feet and ensure that no one sees them because subconsciously they may realise what can be revealed about themselves through their feet.

Just because someone is having a sleep on the beach, doing some yoga or sit ups in the gym, does not give you permission to read their feet. Just because you can (after reading this book) does not mean you should!

Always pay attention to your intention. Is it your intention to care more about them or to pry? Is it to have a better understanding of someone or are you just being nosey? Remember that what you give out you get back, so check within yourself about why you are foot or hand reading and what you want to get out of it. Do unto others as you wish to be done by!

I now pay attention to when I see feet and often look away as I may know 'stuff' that they may not wish me to know. It can be an invasion of their privacy. Just think it through before you launch into a full foot reading session or start scanning their feet for information that they may not wish you to know.

This applies to all situations where you may just happen to see people's feet including:

- Gym and fitness studios

- Shoe shops

- Beach

- Beauty salons

- Dance classes

- Photographs

- Glossy magazines

- Yoga

- Martial arts studios

- Swimming pools

- Relaxation classes

- Anyone in the summer with bare feet or sandals

It is different if someone has come to see you professionally as you may use the knowledge that you read in their feet to help and assist them. However you may or may not say how you have gained this information as it may be too personal. It does help you to build a rapport and connection with your clients. Foot reading can make it easier to work as a team to find solutions and ways of change that achieve their purpose for coming to see you in the first place.

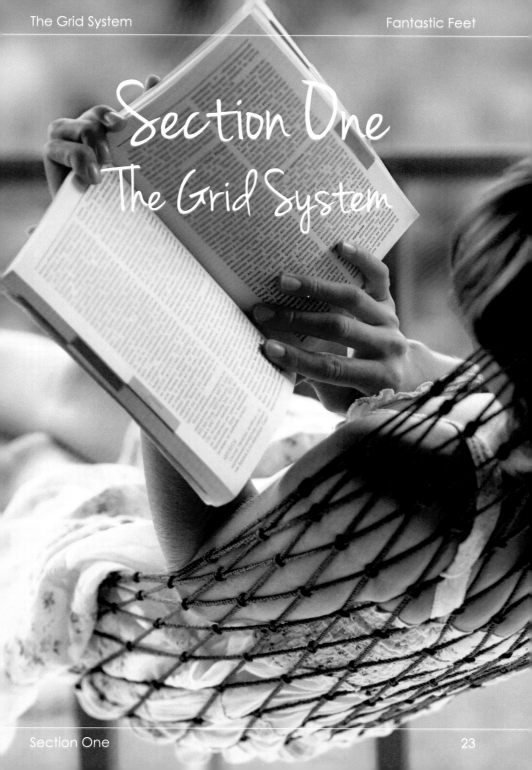

Section One
The Grid System

Vertical Foot Grid

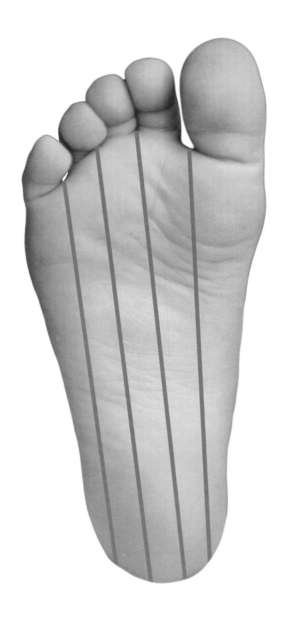

The Grid System

Vertical Grid

We begin by imagining five equal divisions across each foot, known as vertical zones. You may find it easier to practise this by drawing these out on a piece of paper. Each of the four lines that you draw down from between the toes divides the foot into five areas. These areas or sections will show how they relate to various aspects of life and how we live it.

 A note for reflexologists

These zones also relate to the zones identified by Dr William Fitzgerald that are often numbered 1-5.

Vertical Foot Grid Themes

Each of these zones relates to one of the following:

- Thoughts

- Feelings

- Creativity or 'doings'

- Communication

- Family and security

1. Everything that goes down from and including the big toe (hallux) relates to our thoughts and how we are thinking.

2. Everything down from and including the second toe relates to our feelings and how we feel about our life.

3. Everything down from and including the third toe relates to how you do things and how you creatively handle your life.

from
toe to
heel

4. Everything down from and including the fourth toe relates to how you communicate with both yourself and others.

5. Everything down from and including the fifth toe (little toe) relates to how you relate to your family and how secure or genuinely confident (not brash confidence) you are.

Both Feet Themes

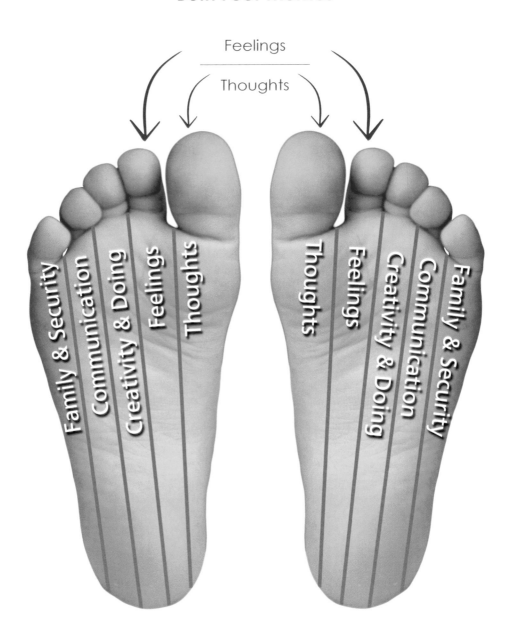

The Other Foot!

Luckily for us the same interpretations relate to both feet, so all it requires is for you to learn the five sectors and then these can be applied to either foot.

Therefore each:

- Big toe / hallux relates to thoughts

- Second toe relates to feelings

- Third toe relates to creativity and doings

- Fourth toe relates to communications

- Five (little) toe relates to the family and security

Vertical Hand Grid

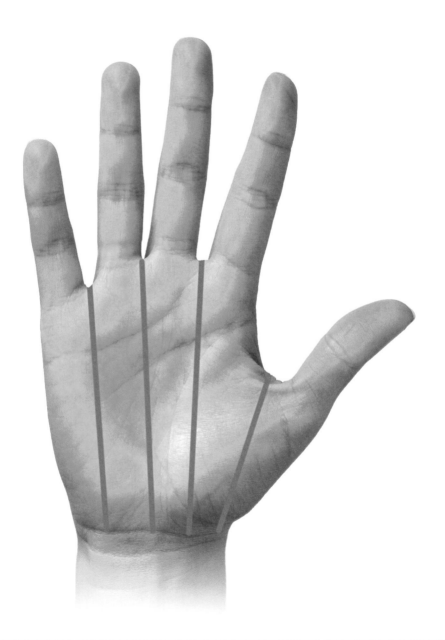

Hands Too

Fortunately we can use the same grid information overlaid on the hands too.

Therefore each:

- Thumb relates to thoughts

- Index finger relates to feelings

- Middle finger relates to creativity and doings

- Fourth (ring) finger relates to communication

- Little finger relates to family and security

Vertical Hand Grid Themes

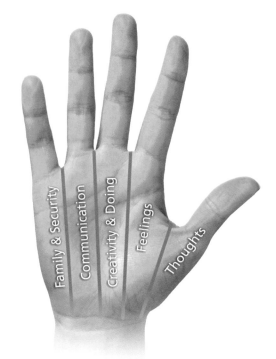

Horizontal Foot Grid

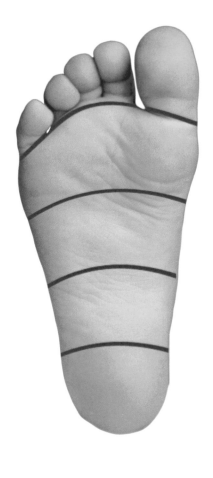

Horizontal Hand Grid

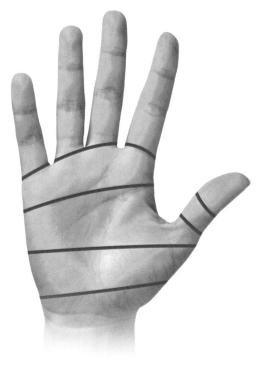

Horizontal Grid

Now imagine five equal divisions down each foot or hand, known as horizontal zones. Again you may find it easier to practise this by drawing these out on a piece of paper. Each of the four lines that you draw across the foot/hand, divides it into five areas. As before these areas or sections will show how they relate to various aspects of life and how we live it.

Each of these zones relate to one of the following:

- Thoughts

- Feelings

- Creativity or 'doings'

- Communication

- Family and security

(See over for more details)

🐾 A note for reflexologists

These divisions on the feet also relate to the areas that are taught in some reflexology courses:

- Shoulder girdle

- Diaphragm line

- Waist line

- Pelvic girdle

Horizontal Foot Grid Themes

- All the toes relate to our thoughts and what we are thinking about.

- All of the ball of the foot relates to our feelings and our senses.

- Most of the middle and arch of the foot relates to our creativity and what we are doing about things.

- The lower half of the arch of the foot relates to all aspects of communication of our lives.

- The heel area relates to how we feel about our family and extended family and how secure and confident we are.

across
the
whole
foot

Horizontal Hand Grid Themes

- All the fingers relate to our thoughts and what we are thinking about.

- All of the fleshy pad below the fingers relates to our feelings and our senses.

- The middle area (natural fold of your hand) relates to our creativity and what we are doing about things.

- The fleshy area of the heel of your hand relates to all aspects of communication of our lives.

- The wrist area relates to how we feel about our family and extended family and how secure and confident we are.

across
the
whole
hand

Vertical and Horizontal Grids Combined

Plantar Aspect

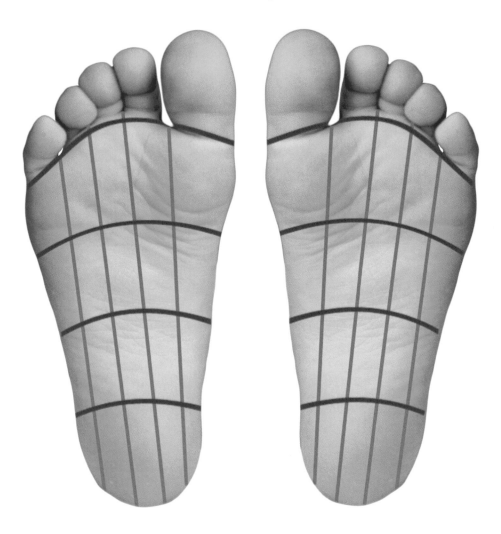

Full Grid

These same five themes, (thoughts, feelings, etc) now relate both vertically and horizontally providing us with a new grid to work from. When we overlay this grid over each foot we get a representation of the aspects of each person's life, skills and experiences which can be read on their feet.

The same is also true when looking at both the top (dorsal aspect) of the feet as well as the sole (plantar aspect) of the feet.

Dorsal Aspect

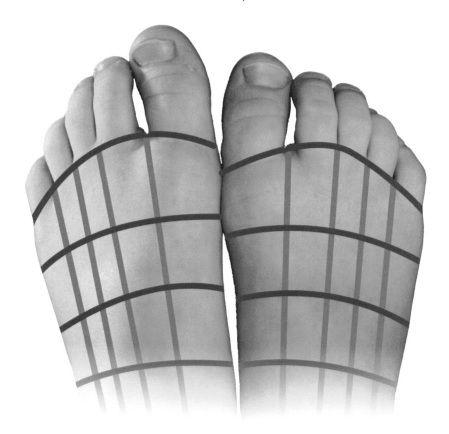

Double Sectors

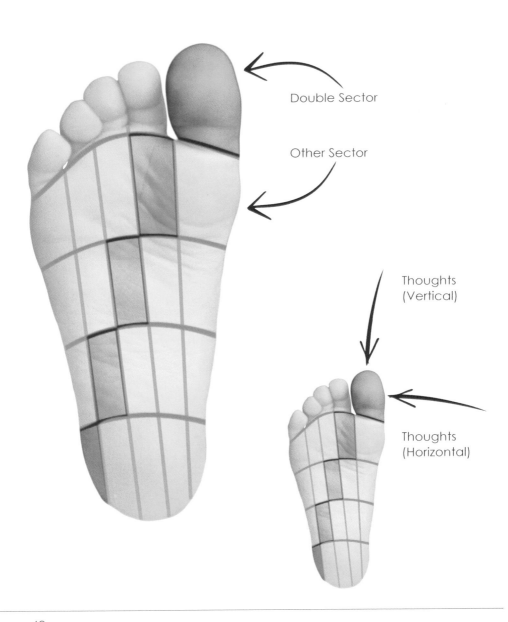

Double Sector

Other Sector

Thoughts
(Vertical)

Thoughts
(Horizontal)

Double Sectors

The grid, adjacent, highlights the double sectors.

A double space is so called because when you overlay the vertical and horizontal grid, you get five specific areas that relate to the same theme in both axis.

These double sectors relate to areas of prime importance for the following:

- Thoughts and quality of the thoughts and thinking
- Feelings and emotions being experienced
- Their creativity and ways of getting this done
- Communication with all (including self)
- Family connections and how confident / secure they feel

This means that when there is a significant mark, colour or noticeable factor found at one of the double spaces, it has double the intensity or meaning.

If any characteristics are within a double space this indicates a very strong link in the person's life.

Pay particular attention if there are any especially noticeable indications on these double areas. Things to look out for and notice include:

- Any extra large toe or toe area
- Patches or areas of hard skin
- Noticeably stronger colour
- Imperfections and skin conditions
- Anything stuck to the person's foot, for example, sock fluff, grass, paper etc.
- Lines
- Indentations
- Swelling

When any of these or anything else that is really noticeable appears on any of the double grid spaces then this indicates more intensive or significant aspects of their life, issues, strengths or capacities.

Dual Theme Sectors

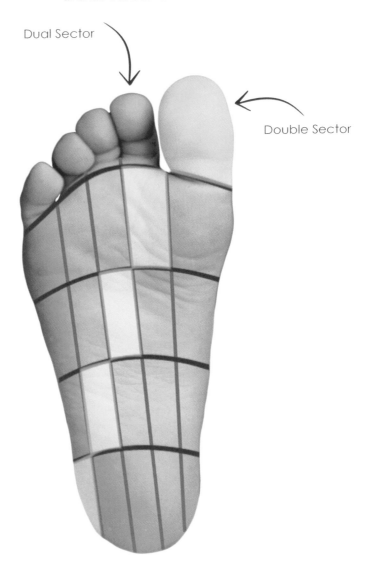

Dual Sector

Double Sector

Dual Theme Sectors

This new grid indicates where all of the key areas are and also shows that some sectors have 'dual' themes (ie thoughts + feelings). Every area of the foot, except the double sectors, has a relationship to two themes, aspects, or abilities in life.

For example, the second toe relates to how a person thinks about what they are feeling, or how they feel about what they are thinking.

The second toe is related to thoughts because the horizontal theme relates to what type of thoughts we are having. It also relates to feelings because the vertical theme relates to feelings and our emotions.

The same double and dual themes apply to the hands too. Each hand has five double sectors as per the feet. Every other hand sector has dual themes as the feet do.

Dual Sectors

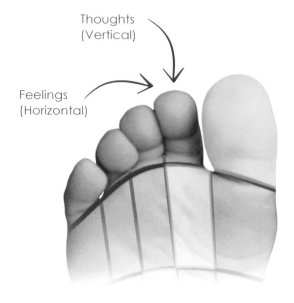

Thoughts (Vertical)

Feelings (Horizontal)

Hand Palmar Grids

Showing double sectors highlighted

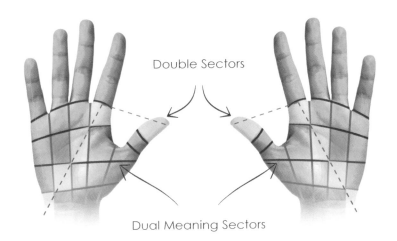

Double Sectors

Dual Meaning Sectors

Hand Dorsal Grids

Showing double sectors highlighted

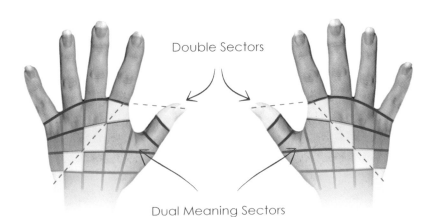

Double Sectors

Dual Meaning Sectors

Foot Plantar Grids

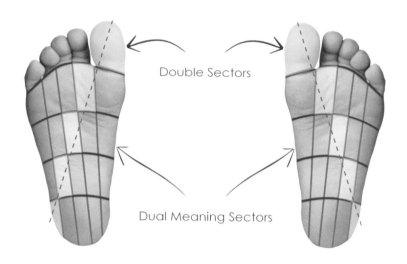

Double Sectors

Dual Meaning Sectors

Foot Dorsal Grids

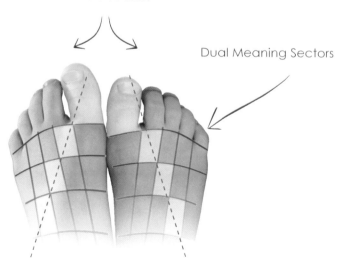

Double Sectors

Dual Meaning Sectors

Sector Meanings

 ## 'Thoughts' Means

- What the person is thinking about
- The level or intensity of thinking. This could mean anything from being very stressed, thinking far too much, to being very relaxed and mindfully peaceful
- Quality of thought action, e.g. 'head stuff'
- General thought patterns and habitual thinking
- Thought energy levels which could show they are mentally spent or mentally energised

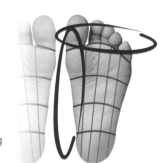

 ## 'Feelings' Means

- Their emotion or emotions
- What they get (or are) emotional about
- How they are feeling
- How they are coping
- The degree of intensity of their feelings
- The energy that is in motion 'e/motion'

 ## 'Creativity and Doing' Means

- What they are doing in their life
- What they are doing about 'it'
- How they get by in life
- What they do and how they operate
- Creative ways of living
- Creative ways of doing

'Communication' Means

Communicating with others via:

- Speech
- Tone
- Words / language
- Body language
- Energetically
- Writing
- Actions

Communication with self via:

- Internal language
- Congruency – belief and actions agree (or not!)
- The chatterbox inside one's head
- Internal reactions or physical discomfort acting as an alert

Communication also includes listening skills too.

'Family and Security' Means

- How confident they feel about themselves
- How important family is to them
- How they feel they fit into the family
- Their level of dependence or independence
- Their links to wider families, for example, church, social networks, community

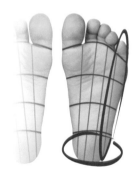

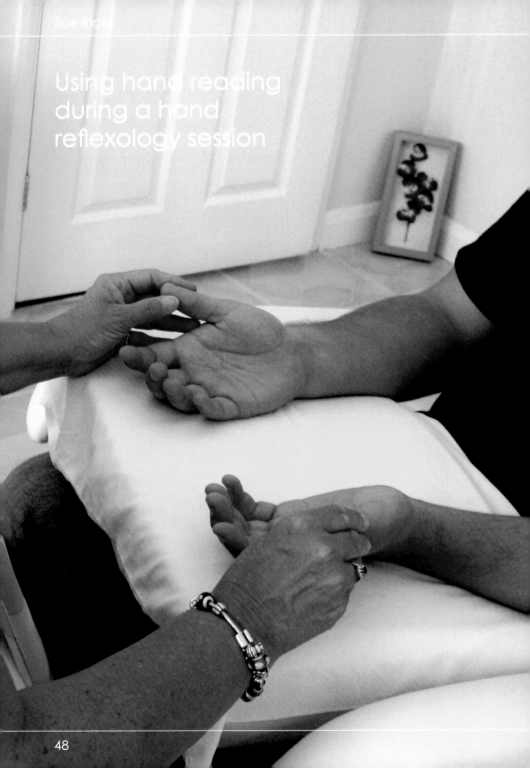

Using hand reading during a hand reflexology session

Section Two
Colours

Hand and Feet Colours

We can get a great deal of information from the colours of the feet or hands.

This can mean an all over colour or even a subtle shade or tone (hue). It could mean colour variations in different areas of the foot with some sectors or small areas showing a distinct colour or hue.

Any colour that can be seen on or within the foot is significant and can tell us much about the factors being experienced by a person. This includes the obvious and subtle tones of the feet plus more transient indicators such as items that have apparently been randomly stuck to the foot.

Pay attention to any colour or hue that appears and any items on the foot as these could give greater insight.

I have seen some great examples of things stuck onto the feet. These include a price ticket for a lollipop over an area relating to how valued a lady felt!

I remember a lady who had grass across the lower half of her instep (and nowhere else). This related to how jealous she was feeling about how others could speak out but she could not, ("it's all right for you" etc).

I met a bride who had a bit of confetti on her foot. It was a gold heart shape that was right over her feelings double zone and this was three weeks after her wedding. She had no idea how it had got there!

We can tell much about people and their lives from the colours that we observe on their feet. These colour changes may occur over a period of time or even before or after treatments. Sometimes the colour can change whilst chatting to the person and this may show how they truly feel about the topic of conversation.

These colours or colour hues can be seen in everyone, irrespective of their overall skin colour. What we are looking for is any variation or deviation from the persons' natural skin tone.

Orange

Purple

White

Colour Chart

Red	=	Angry or embarrassed
Yellow	=	Fed up
Orange	=	Frustration
Blue	=	Hurt
Black	=	Extreme hurt
Brown	=	Browned off
Green	=	Jealously or envy
Purple	=	Bruised emotions
White	=	Exhausted, withdrawn, empty, washed out
Natural Colour	=	In the pink, happy and healthy

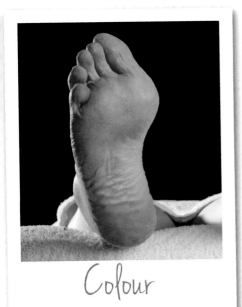

Colour

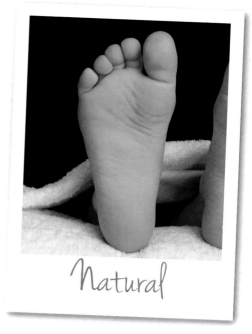

Natural

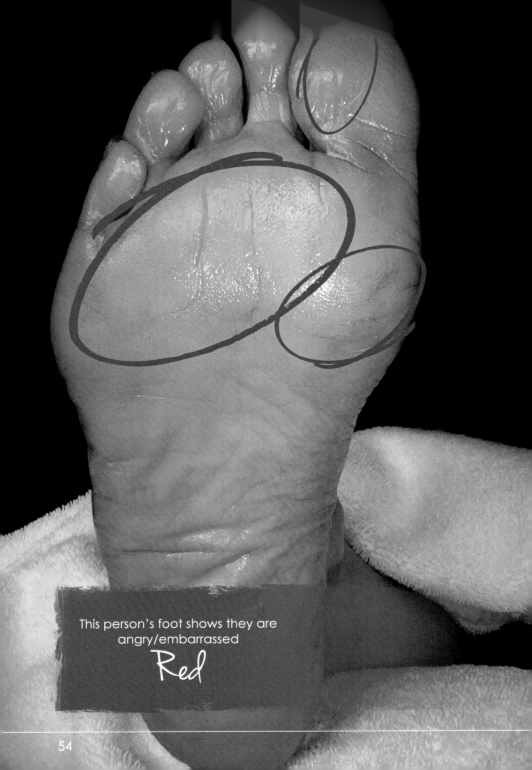

This person's foot shows they are
angry/embarrassed

Red

Red – (Anger or Embarrassment)

This is seen when someone is feeling quite annoyed or even angry. The deeper the red, the deeper emotion is felt.

This could mean that:

- They are angry with themselves or others
- They are embarrassed about themselves or others
- It could be a combination of both; they are angry at being embarrassed or they are embarrassed that they are angry

This can be as a result of an unusual way of living i.e. they are always angry with life.

or

A specific incident, experience or occurrence has triggered feelings of anger or embarrassment.

Examples:

1. A person may become embarrassed over something whilst in public resulting in them blushing bright red, leading them to feel angry with him or herself. This would show as the colour red (scarlet) on their feet as they initially experienced embarrassment followed by anger with themselves.

2. A person may be embarrassed because they have lost their temper. This again would show as red on their feet due to both emotions being experienced.

3. Anyone who is self critical and gets angry with themselves will have red toes most of the time as they are experiencing angry thoughts much of the time. The intensity of colour may alter according to the degree of thoughts at any one time.

This person's foot shows they
are feeling fed up
Yellow

Yellow – (Fed Up)

"I am fed up with all this."

This is seen when someone is fed up. The more fed up they are, the deeper, stronger or brighter the yellow will be.

One way some students remember this easily is a little rude, but it works! As yellow is the colour of urine, some remember it as "pissed off". So if someone is feeling fed up they will have areas of yellow on their feet. This is often found over the balls of their feet (the 'feeling' areas) or on their toes (their 'thoughts').

This could mean that:

- A person is fed up in general

or

- They are fed up with a specific situation

Examples:

1. Someone is feeling thoroughly fed up with life in general. This would show with yellow being the most noticeable or prominent colour over the whole foot or feet.

2. When someone is thinking about the issues in their life that they are fed up about, then their toes will be yellow. It can be helpful to notice which toes are affected as it may be all their toes or just some. The relevant toe(s) shows you what aspect of their life they are thinking about and are fed up with.

3. A person may be fed up with coping and have too much on, so they cover up their feelings with lots of hard, protective yellow skin. The more layers of yellow they have, the more the person is protecting themselves and their feelings or thoughts.

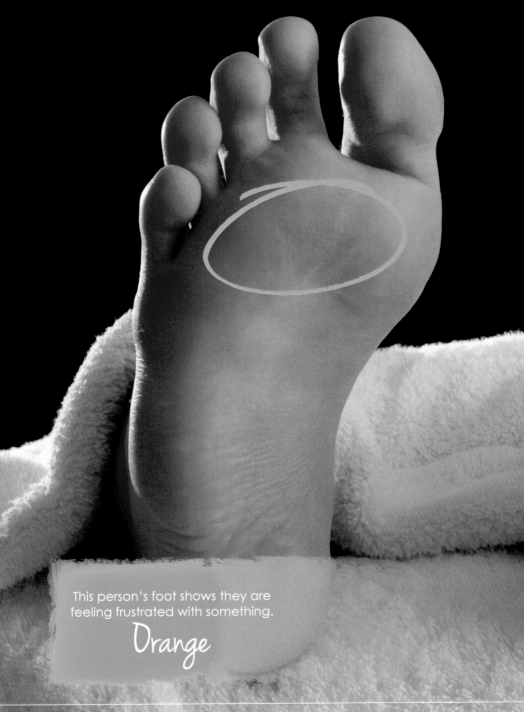

This person's foot shows they are
feeling frustrated with something.

Orange

Orange – (Frustrated or Annoyed)

"For goodness sake, just get on with it."

This is seen when someone is frustrated with an issue or with life. Again, the deeper or more vibrant the colour, the more annoyance and frustration it reflects.

Orange is a combination of the colours red and yellow. It is therefore a combination of the meanings of both 'red' (anger or embarrassment) and 'yellow' (fed up).

This could mean that:

- A person is experiencing real annoyance about a situation and is fed up about it too.

or

- They are really fed up about it and getting annoyed at being "pissed off."

or

- They are annoyed and frustrated about an issue and fed up with it too.

Examples:

1. A person may have the decorators in and be annoyed that it is taking so long. They are now totally fed up with it and wish it would all just go away. They are both annoyed (angry = 'red') and fed up ('yellow') which together will be shown as 'orange.'

2. Someone may be trying to do something and it is just not working out. The harder they try, the more elusive the project becomes and they feel like giving up. This would be shown with orange throughout the balls of their feet, especially under their second ('feeling') and third ('doing') toes. It may be that the colour is more prominent on their third toe, with hard skin to protect themselves, their feelings and thoughts.

3. A parent may be getting totally wound up about their children and their behaviour. They find themselves getting wound up and totally fed up with the noise or mess they make. The combination of being really annoyed (anger / red) and fed up (yellow) creates orange looking feet especially over the ball of the foot ('feelings') and possibly around the heel ('family') and little toe.

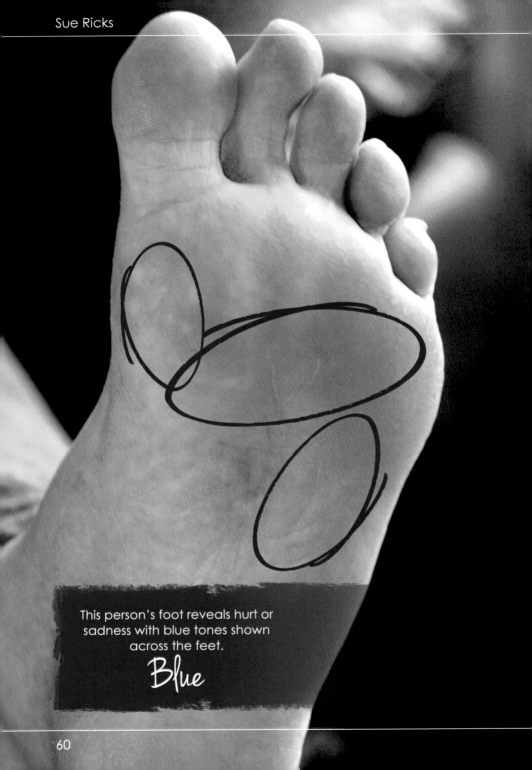

This person's foot reveals hurt or sadness with blue tones shown across the feet.

Blue

Blue – (Hurt)

"Ouch, that hurts"

This is seen when there has been an element of hurt in their life. It may be that the person has been hurt and the memories are still strong or perhaps that they are currently hurting.

It could mean that:

- The person was hurt in the past and it still hurts

or

- The person is in a current situation that hurts

Examples:

1. A person may have been in a failed relationship and never really got over it. The pain and the feelings of hurt may be clearly seen on the feet many years later. An underlying hue of blue may be seen below the surface indicating their old hurt that is still there but has not been processed or healed.

2. A person might have felt rejected as a child and have bad memories of early childhood and now they are feeling rejected again by a relative or friend. This would look more intensely blue as it is both old hurt combined with being hurt again.

3. A person may have received news of something that hurts or experienced a difficult conversation. This could show as a blue tint of colour across the lower instep area ('communication') of the feet.

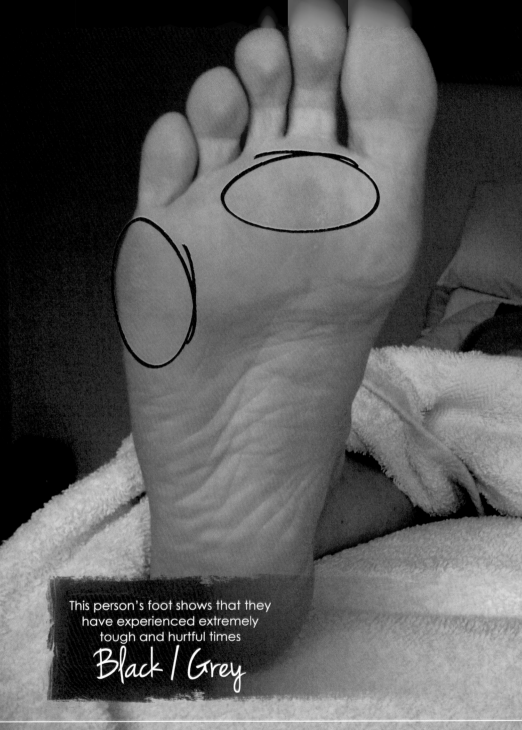

This person's foot shows that they have experienced extremely tough and hurtful times

Black / Grey

Black / Grey – (Extreme Hurt)

"Don't go there, that hurts too much"

This is seen when there has been a deeper hurt that may or may not be consciously felt by the individual concerned. Sometimes this level of hurt goes a very long way back in to their past and may relate to social values, conditioning, and experiences that have impacted on them. These may have hindered and affected them as a child and is continuing into their adulthood causing hurt in their current life.

It could mean that:

- The person was deeply hurt by events, experiences and memories of the past.
- The person is affected by a current situation or experience that hurts them deeply.

Examples:

1. A person may have been brought up being told that they must be seen and not heard. This way of living may have taught them that they were and are devalued and worthless. If they have not worked through that type of conditioning then these feelings of deep hurt will still show below the surface as a dark hue.

2. A child may have lost a well loved relative at an early age and felt a profound sense of loss that hurt them deeply. This may still be visible on or in their feet even years later. Interestingly enough it may become even more prominent when the adult is experiencing times that relate to their earlier trauma. For example, they may be facing their own or loved ones health challenges, a fear of dying in other ways or bankruptcy.

3. An individual may have witnessed a trauma and felt overwhelmed by it and be suffering the deep hurt of the experience. Unless the individual seeks professional help or finds their own way of dealing with it, then the colour will either be there all the time or come back whenever they are reminded of it.

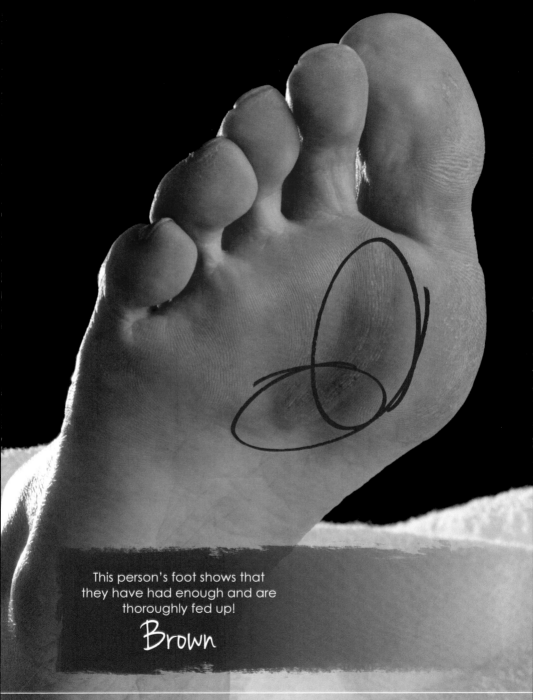

This person's foot shows that they have had enough and are thoroughly fed up!

Brown

Brown – (Browned Off, Exceptionally Fed Up)

"I have had enough."

This is seen when someone is totally browned off. This is a deeper emotion and is truly beyond being fed up.

Brown is like a deeper shade of yellow (fed up) and therefore they are totally and utterly fed up with something.

If there is an area where there appears to be a 'spot' of colour this may indicate the source of their issue. Alternatively, it may be that there are several layers of colours, causing this 'spot'. A 'spot' colour has been likened to looking like a drop of paint, splodged on a part of their foot.

It could mean that:

- The person always feels totally fed up and that has become their 'norm' or habitual way of living and feeling.
- The person has recently had cause to feel really thoroughly fed up.

Examples:

1. A person may be struggling to cope with a relation's crisis that is affecting them. For example, someone's parent may have become housebound. They may have chosen to do everything possible and be there for their beloved parent, but at the same time there may be feelings of being fed up with the constant responsibility. They love the person but are missing out on their own life and feel totally fed up with it. It is not resentment or anger with the parent or situation as this would show as 'red.'

2. A person has learnt to adapt to another person's ways of living and therefore taken an easier life rather than challenging their significant other. They just keep their mouth shut and get on with it. Yet underneath they are really and truly fed up with living this way. In this instance we may notice areas of brown shading across the ball of the foot or around the heel or toes.

3. Some people find it difficult to actually get on and do things, even though they have the desire to do them. This may make them feel either frustrated ('orange') or totally fed up with themselves ('brown') and will be shown particularly on their middle toe ('creativity and doings'). This often affects their right middle toe more than their left.

This person's foot has a gentle greenish hue indicating a level of jealousy - i.e. wishing things were different

Green

Green – (Envy or Jealousy)

"It's alright for you."

This is seen when someone is experiencing some element of jealously or envy of someone or something.

It could mean that:

- The person has always lived their life like that and it is almost a family or cultural trait. It has developed into a habitual way of thinking and/or feeling.
- The person has a specific reason to feel jealous or envious.

Examples:

1. An individual may feel disadvantaged as they sense or believe that everyone else has had a better start in life. When they feel that things are not fair, their feet may have a subtle greenish hue to them. This is an underlying colour tint to the sole of their foot. If this jealous or envious emotion has led them to feel angry, they may have red markings on their feet too.

2. If an individual was striving for a better life for themselves and saw others had got there first, it can cause jealousy that others had achieved it and the person concerned had not. In this instance, the tops of their toes ('thoughts') and mid arch ('doings') area may have a subtle tone to it. This will disappear once the focus returns to achieving it rather than being jealous.

3. A person may want a specific thing and be envious of anyone else who has it. It may be a particular job, life style or car. When the feelings of envy are high the level and vibrancy of the colour green increases. Likewise, as the envy or jealousy reduces, the colour becomes less obvious and more subtle.

The grass is always greener on the other side.

This person's foot shows they are experiencing a time of difficulty that is emotionally challenging.

Purple

Purple – (Bruised Emotions)

"That really upsets me."

This is seen when someone has bruised emotions or feels bruised with some experience, event or memory.

It could mean that:

- The person has lived for a long while carrying the upset that they feel inside resulting from an earlier period of their lives.
- The person has recently had an experience that has left them feeling 'bruised' emotionally. Some describe it as feeling that their emotions have been 'battered'.
- Someone may feel that their emotions, values or beliefs have not been recognised, acknowledged or taken in to account

Examples:

1. An individual may feel that their view is not valued or listened to when in discussion with a partner.

2. A child may seek to please in all cases so as to avoid any feelings evoked if someone is displeased with them.

3. A person is advancing in age and is not happy with how life is changing around and for them. This can be a change of reality that can feel quite distressing.

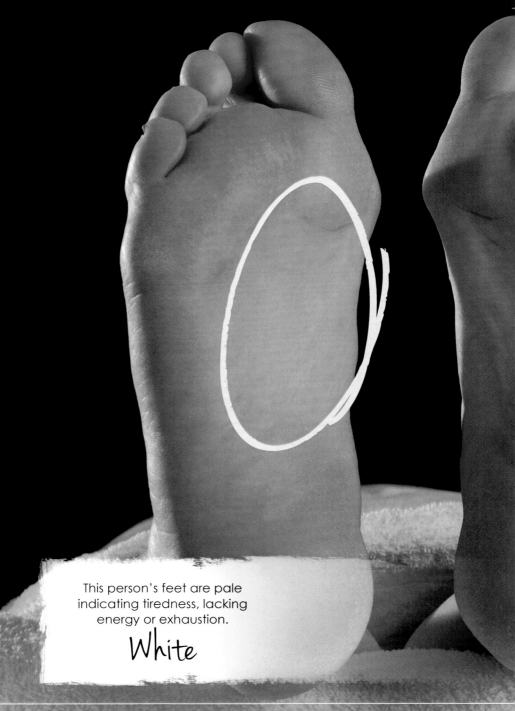

This person's feet are pale indicating tiredness, lacking energy or exhaustion.

White

White – (Washed Out / Exhausted)

"I have nothing left to give."

People's feet go or appear white or paler than normal when they are lacking in energy or withdrawn. They could also be feeling exhausted. Essentially their reserves are being used to cope with whatever they are dealing with.

It could mean that:

- A person has a great deal to manage and arrange and has always lived their life like that. It is almost a family or cultural trait and it may be normal to give too much.
- The person is experiencing an event or occurrence that requires extra input or energy. This huge effort may be exhausting the individual concerned.

Examples:

1. A mother may be exhausted with caring for all of the members of her family. She may have been working long hours to get her work done and has neglected herself. Her vitality may be low and so there is little colour to her feet. As she picks up and her energy returns, so the colour of her feet will improve.

2. A child may have chosen to withdraw inside themselves as they do not feel comfortable allowing others to see or hear them. This causes their feet to become quite pale.

3. A person may feel as if they have given everything to a project or occasion and feel totally wiped out.

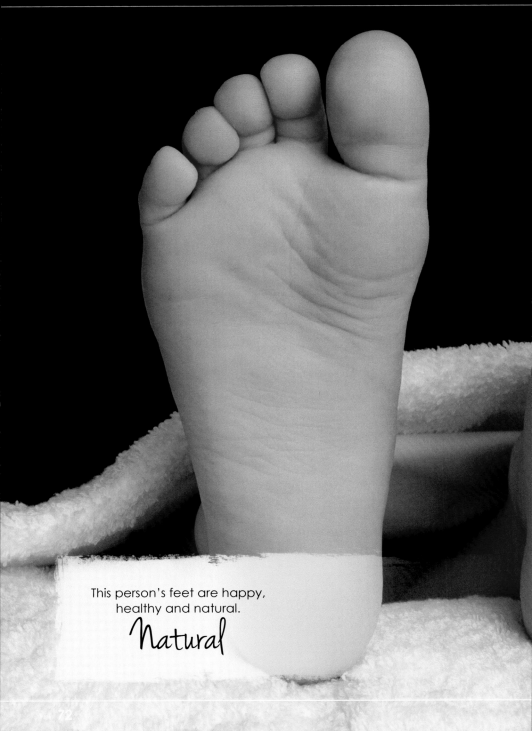

This person's feet are happy,
healthy and natural.

Natural

Natural Colour / Pink – Happy and Healthy

"I feel great, life is good."

When a small and happy child is relaxed and playing, their feet will be a lovely natural or pink colour. There will just be their natural skin tone with no variations or spots of colours, colour hues or accent colours.

Pure, lovely, natural looking feet.

This is what happens to people's feet of all ages when they are living a happy and healthy life and feel emotionally strong, resilient and capable. They are enjoying life, know that they are on their path and trusting that all is going appropriately for themselves and their life.

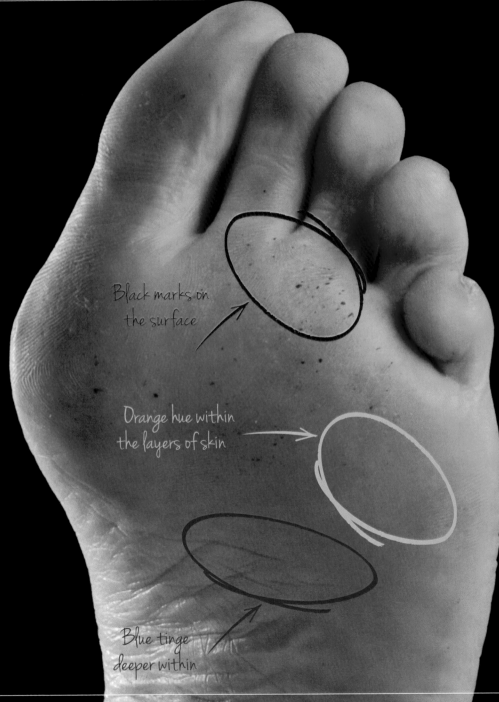

Black marks on
the surface

Orange hue within
the layers of skin

Blue tinge
deeper within

Colours and Observations

It is important to note the colour of someone's foot, toes or feet in general.

Pay attention to the colour in a variety of places or ways including:

- On the surface
- Within the layers of the skin
- Colours that seem to come from deep inside the foot
- Spot colours
- The colour of anything that has attached itself to the foot, for example sock fluff, grass etc.

Depth of Colour

The stronger or brighter the colour, the more intense the emotion and, therefore, it is of greater significance.

The deeper 'down' the colour appears, the deeper the issue is. Some colours appear to come to the surface as issues come up and are resolved or are ready to be resolved.

Repeated Colours

Some people re-experience their learning opportunities time and time again until they get it right. For example, when we learn the lesson of an experience, action or behaviour, then the lesson goes away. When we do not recognise what we are doing, how we attracted these circumstances or created the experience then the opportunity to learn crops up time and time again. Some call this 'cycles of behaviour'. If we do not change (actions, behaviour or beliefs etc.) then nothing changes. In these cases of repeating mistakes or patterns of life then we will see the same colours appearing or remaining time after time.

Colour Change in Action

If you notice your (or someone else's) first toe is quite red (anger) for example, it may be a good opportunity to look at a situation in other ways, i.e. reframe.

A great reframe or way of altering a thought could be from:

a. *"How dare you speak to me like that? That is untrue. I am furious"* – (Red = anger, furious)

to

b. *"Maybe he or she is really struggling and that is why they are shouting at me like that. Actually I know what they have just said to me is not true and maybe later we can go through the facts and find out what is really wrong and maybe clear the air"* – (Natural colour as there are no heated emotions.)

Or a minor shift or reframe:

c. *"Oh no – I am going to be late now as I am stuck in this traffic hold up"* (Red)

to

d. *"Now that I have time to reflect on things, relax and clear my head. I am also glad that I am sitting here and not in the cause of the hold-up"*

Another example:

e. *"I was going to do that job but the mail delivery with the essential item has not arrived. I am in trouble as I cannot do the job now."*

to

f. *"Maybe I am meant to be doing something else and it's a good opportunity to practice relaxation (deep breathing) while stressed! After that I will be okay and in a better mental and emotional place to get the job done."*

It is really interesting that our feet (and hands) show us how we are doing and also show us how quickly our body responds to the type of thoughts that we have.

One of my clients kept talking about how her family did not really notice her and respect her point of view. She felt ignored and it made her feel angry and upset inside. The more we talked throughout our session the more she came to wonder if she too ignored the other members of the family's view point and maybe ignored them too. She tried paying more attention to them and what they said and noticed that they paid more attention to her as well. The more she listened to her Mum and Dad, the more she found herself beginning to get what their point of view was. Previously she had found her brother to be rude and unpleasant to her but when talking to her Dad she wondered if the reason was actually that her brother was struggling with lack of self belief and only getting at her when it got too much. This changed my clients perspective and she found that she was more understanding and caring of her brother and less likely to take it personally when he tried to be deliberately rude to her. Her feet changed colour accordingly. She went from having an underlying blue tinge with red areas (hurt and anger) to pale orange as she experienced frustration with herself and also for her family.

Her breakthrough was in realising she could not control or manage her family, but what she could do was to be the kind of person she wanted to be, mind her own business and do her best for herself and others.

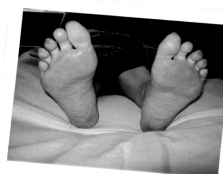

Red

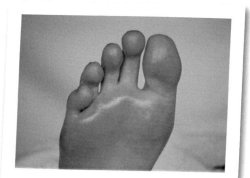

Orange

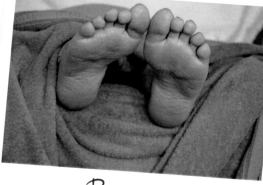

Brown

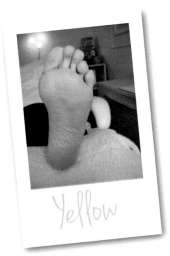

Yellow

Section Three
Shape of the Feet

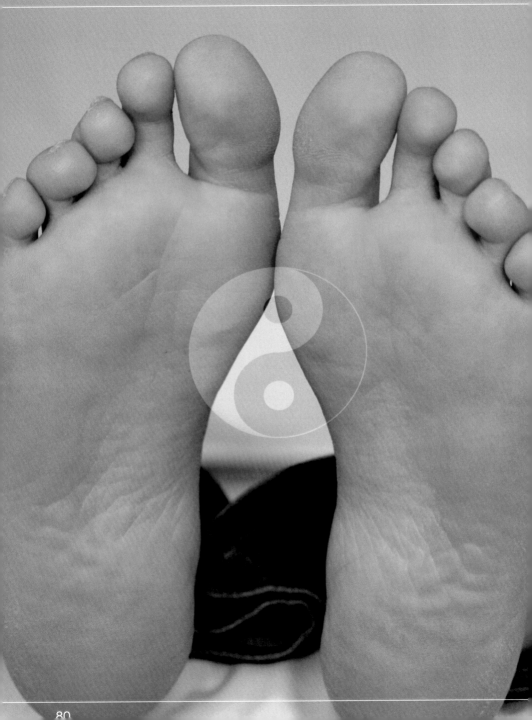

Right Foot and Left Foot

Right Foot	Left Foot
The right foot generally relates to the yang, masculine, active and dominant aspects of life.	The left foot relates to the yin, feminine, passive, nurturing aspects of life.
The right foot is more about doing things and actions...	...whilst the left foot is more about caring for self and nurturing.
The right foot relates to your male parent figure and how you relate to males.	The left foot relates to your female parent figure and how you relate to females.

The sole of your foot represents who you are now. You are the sum of your life's experiences, decisions, beliefs and actions.

Right Foot	Left Foot
Yang	Yin
Active	Passive
Others	Self
Doings	Nurturing
Relationships with Males	Relationships with Females

The above tables are shown from a reflexologist perspective when they look at a client's feet.

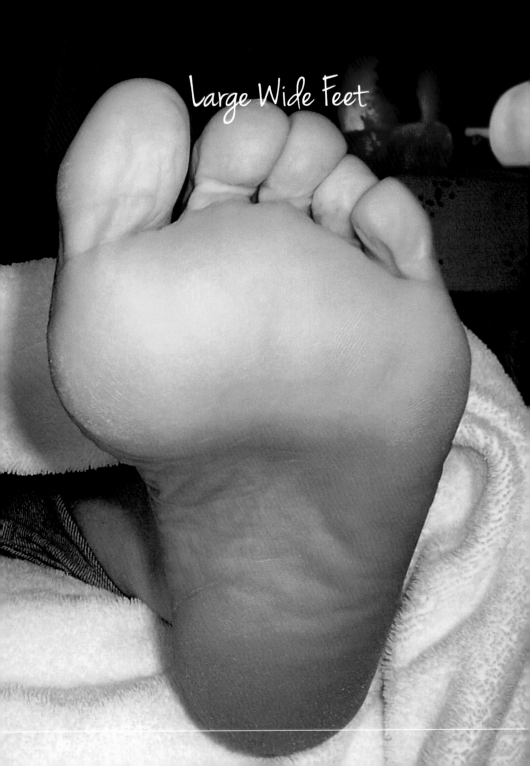

Large Wide Feet

Size of Feet

The size of a person's feet becomes important if their feet are larger or smaller than average. This is especially true if their feet seem to be disproportionate to the persons general build and size.

Big Feet

The bigger the foot, the bigger the impression that they are making or can make. They are able to make a difference and have more resources to draw on. (Their foot contains more as it is larger).

- They can make a big impact
- Potential is huge as the larger the foot the larger their potential.
- They can make a difference to both self and others.

The larger the foot, the bigger their potential. Potential to help others, do well in their career and generally 'make a difference'.

I have been teaching for many years and have met some wonderful people who are in well paid and responsible high powered jobs and yet their soul yearns to 'make a difference'. One lady said that she is good at her job, she can do it easily, she is very well paid and yet it offers nothing to the world. She wants to explore training in reflexology so that she can learn how to do something that helps others and makes a difference to them.

A person with a larger foot is more in tune with what 'makes a difference' rather than simply doing a good job. They understand how their actions impact on others and hopefully (if they have sufficient confidence) will create opportunities to do things that help the wider community.

Sadly some people with big feet may have been repressed in their younger years. They may have spoken out on behalf of the bigger picture, world impact, industry focus, or wider family community and may have been misunderstand by their peers or elders. Adulthood gives the potential for making the most of these qualities.

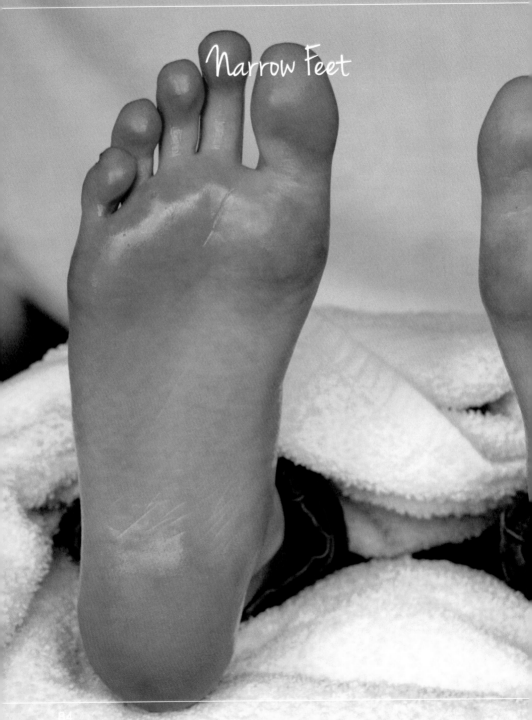

Narrow Feet

Small Feet

Someone with small feet will be a more delicate person who may find subtle ways of making a difference. Often said to be more artistic and gentle.

- Can be subtle in their impact on the world, therefore very powerful
- Delicate
- Is less noticed (hence the Chinese binding of girls feet)
- Can be over powered if not alert and careful.
- Can be clever at finding ways around tough obstacles

Shape of Feet

The shape of the foot reflects a great deal about the person, their personality, path in life and potential.

Narrow Feet

A person with narrow feet is quite delicate and can make a subtle and potentially important impact on the world by small but significant achievements.

- Often connects with things that other people pass by

- Appreciates the little things in life

- Artistic

- Aesthetic

- Gentle

- Aware

Broad Feet

Broad (Wide) Foot

Broad feet indicate the person's dependability.

The location of the 'width' is important too as it shows how the person demonstrates their dependability. See below how this applies to different parts of the foot.

- Whole foot – When the whole foot is broad and wide, this indicates that the person is dependable and reliable in all areas of life. They will be a down to earth individual who is both practical and works hard. This is an excellent person to turn to in a crisis and therefore is someone who is often found managing church fetes, fund raising events etc.

- Top of foot – A foot that is wide at the top (toes) is someone who is able to think about a broad range of issues.

- Ball of foot – A foot that is broad at the level of the ball of the foot (feelings) is someone who respects other people's feelings. They will be the person who everyone comes to for help as they have plenty of knowledge for feelings of self and others. This is because this person is seen as having a 'broad' shoulder to cry on.

- Arch of foot – A larger than normal width across the arch of the foot is found when the person can be relied on to speak out and be a good spokesperson. This is not found too often as generally everyone needs to speak out on their own behalf.

- Base of foot – Someone will have a foot that is wide at the base if they are very family minded. They will feel confident about themselves in their family and provide a secure base for family members to rely on.

Angled Feet – Facing In or Out

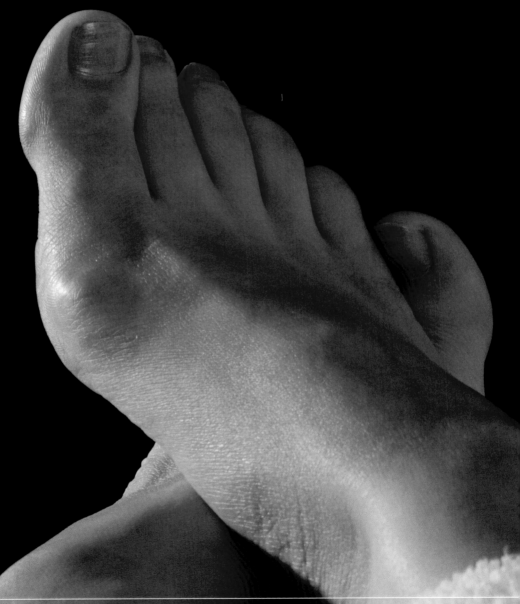

Angled Feet

Angled feet means feet that fall in or out when resting or when the person is standing. The angle that the feet lie in reflects the subconscious of the person's feelings of confidence and contentment. This is equally appropriate with people standing sitting or relaxing.

Below describes the differing ways the feet can be and their interpretations:

- Left foot turned out – means that there are female influences that have pulled them off track. Maybe trying to conform and be accepted by female 'rules, codes and expectations'.

- Right foot turned out – means that there are male influences that have pulled them off track. The person maybe trying to conform and be adopting male or authoritarian principles.

- Both feet turned out – when both feet fall out it indicates that the person is aiming to come across as in control and on track. They are following a way of life that is not natural to them, that can lead to feelings of vulnerability which they are unwilling or unable to mask. It can be a sign of 'bluffing it' as the person is sitting with their legs or feet wide apart as an act of bravado, "here is everything exposed". Whereas, in reality, it is a way of trying to express bravado and confidence as a distraction (double bluff) from feeling very anxious and too scared to show it. A case of 'bluff and double bluff' as they are off track and have lost their own way. They may not even know this themselves as they need to feel in control and very able to cope.

- Right foot falling in – they have less confidence in dealing with male aspects of life.

- Left foot falling in – they lack confidence on coping with the female aspects of life.

- Both feet falling in – feeling very vulnerable and protective of self and therefore, trying to close themselves in (shy). The more angled they are the more self conscious they feel.

The further out the feet fall, the further off track the person is in the way that they walk forward in their life.

Soles Facing Each Other

When a person's feet face sole to sole (i.e. the weight of their body and foot is on the outer area of the foot) as they sit or walk, this means that they are self protecting. They experience social or family demands on their life and choose to lift their feet (thoughts) slightly away at the instep. Therefore, they:

- Rely on family for protection
- Take on family responsibilities
- Honour family or society pressures
- Pull thoughts back out of reach
- Have hidden depths

Walking on Ball of the Foot – Tip Toes

Someone will pull themselves up onto tip toes when they want to get a raised point of view. Although they want to be noticed, they do not want to disturb anyone. They may avoid confrontation and tip toe round a subject rather just come out with it. Therefore, they:

- Want to be noticed
- Have a higher perspective
- Do not want to disturb
- Are delicate
- Are able to hold their balance
- Are self balancing

Flat Footed

This is sometimes called 'fallen arches' as the arch of their foot has collapsed. The natural shape of the foot is to have a raised area in the middle of the foot that acts as a shock absorber. So, someone who has fallen arches and flat feet has less ability to cope with shocks. They can therefore be very sensitive and protective of self (to avoid shocks) or over controlling to manage life to avoid unwanted surprises. They:

- Like to keep life safe
- Are not able to cope well with change and surprises
- Avoid risks
- Depend on others for safety

Walking on the Outside of Their Feet

They are experiencing pressure from family, society or work. The emphasis of their life and energy is in to family and wider family (e.g. society or groups they belong to). All the force of their connection with the world is through their 'family' and how it is with them. Their own personal thoughts and intelligence are of less importance.

When the bulk of the pressure is on the outside of the foot and into their heel area this shows that they are doing their best and are literally 'digging their heels in' to cope and do it their own way. Meaning:

- Family way of life and rules are important
- Family and security pressures felt
- Digging in has become necessary

Floppy Feet

Floppy feet is when their feet fall about and do not sit or stand up right with little firmness. This means that they lack personal power. They experience life as being something that just happens to them rather than taking control (see rigid feet for opposite approach). This can be a permanent, and therefore a long term issue, or, a transitory time reflecting that they normally have power but at the moment they do not. Therefore, they are:

- Lacking in personal power
- Used to letting people have power over them
- Easily influenced
- Passive – keen to say 'okay – what ever'

You can have feet that are both floppy and angled. This means that they are being self protective and currently lacking in personal power.

Rigid Feet

A person with rigid feet that feel very stiff with no flexibility of movement has learnt to take a rigid and precise view on life. They are tense and managing in the best way they can, however that may have meant creating tight boundaries and ways of living.

They are often people who have learnt to control their environment as much as possible. This is often found in people with high standards who are tireless in their pursuit of getting things right. The level of tension (stiffness or rigidity) is directly related to the amount of internal tension that they are experiencing.

- Tight toes mean they are rigid in outlook
- The tighter or more rigid the feet – the more inner tension
- Like or need to take control
- Can feel unsafe if not in control

I recently met a young man who had quite severe health challenges. He had been recommended to me by a friend's Mum who suggested that a reflexology session may help his self esteem and confidence. I was interested that on the initial meeting he presented himself as a guy who is very much in control and he wanted a clear guideline from me on what to expect and how he should "behave". I was intrigued by his questions which included: "where and how do you want me to sit" and "what do I need to do". On the first touch of his feet, it was evident that he was extremely tense and needed a great deal of information to be able to work out his safety and how to manage and control himself. The reflexology treatments have really helped and by his third session his feet were much more flexible. This also related to an increase in his mental approach and mental flexibility too.

Sometimes a person's desire to control leads to a desire to control more and more. There is a useful phrase that explains that *"constriction leads to extinction"*. The more the need to control and constrict their life, the more chance they have of actually extinguishing their life and dreams – so ideally we work towards moving, happy and flexible feet!

Ticklish Feet

Some people dislike having ticklish feet, whilst others find it makes them giggle. For some it brings out childlike laughter and for others it is an uncomfortable experience.

The key is whether they like it or not. If someone has ticklish feet and it is okay for them then they may be very in tune with things around them.

If someone dislikes it then they may be resistant to being touched and find it hard to relax with physical contact. It is also possible that they may have had a bad experience in the past regarding their feet so have held tension in their feet.

Therefore, they are:

- Very sensitive

- Protective

- Determined to keep their need for protection secret

- Able to withdraw instantly

- Harbouring inner tensions

Temperature

People's feet vary in temperature. Ideally people have nice warm hands and feet; neither too hot nor too cold. Obviously various factors including environment, age and gender can affect the temperature of your hands and feet. However, in foot and hand reading, warm hands or feet mean that the person is living well; enjoying life, loving and feeling loved whilst maintaining their energy.

Hot (burning) hands or feet is an indication of excessive circulatory flow and potentially the body working to release excess heat.

Cold hands or feet mean that there is some compromise or restriction to their circulation.

In foot and hand reading the temperature of the feet relates to circulation, which is blood flow, which comes from the heart and another phrase for the heart is the 'chi flow of love pump'.

Hot hands and feet
- Burning up
- Something is causing real agitation

Hot Feet
- When there is an issue with something that they are passionate about or stand for. When energy has got 'stuck', like when water builds up against a dam.

Hot Hands
- When they are almost trying to handle something that is too hot to handle.

Cold Hands and feet
- The warmth of the loving feelings are not reaching out to their extremities.
- Tension causing restriction in circulation.
- Lack of love (chi) flow. Will improve as love of self and others increases with acceptance.

Cold Feet
- Is about when their beliefs/values (what they stand for) or something of significance or importance isn't happening.

Cold Hands
- When there is an issue with what they are handling or doing. Likely to be something they don't love.

Colour link:
Hot is red ie angry or embarrassed / Cold is white ie exhaustion.

Foot Condition

Cracked Heels

The heel is the family, security and confidence sector of the foot.

Heels = Horizontally – family and security theme / Vertically – all themes

Cracking heels relate to feelings that 'things are cracking up' with regard to family and the security of the family unit.

If the skin cracks around the outside of the heel area then this is a 'double' space. Both areas of the grid are 'family and security' (horizontally and vertically) and therefore anything seen here is of greater significance and importance.

In addition, if the skin is also quite hard through layers of hard skin, this is due to the extra protection required (relating to wanting to feel more confident and secure with family).

Hard skin is found when there is a need to protect the area (like armour plating).

If this skin becomes dry (dehydration means lack of support and nourishment for self) then this can cause the skin to crack and sometimes even bleed.

A crack (or cracks) that bleed often happens on a parent at a time of a child leaving home or growing up and becoming increasingly independent. It is very likely that they appear fine but underneath are struggling. A parent's role is complex and part of it is to ensure that they bring their child up to be independent and fine without them, but the whole process can really hurt the parent. A happy and independent child is a great result and can be one to be proud of. However, the process of separating the child's needs from the parent can be painful and may be apparent with cracked and bleeding heels. The deeper the crack on the heel, the deeper the pain, so the more severe the emotional pain and the bigger the crack and loss of blood.

Cracked Heel

So, let's go back to basics.

Blood is the carrier of chi (energy)

Heart = love, therefore, blood = love chi.

The heart pumps blood through the heart.

Heart = love, therefore the heart = love pump!

Therefore, loss of blood through the cracking of the heels shows deep sadness that is not being expressed but felt very deeply.

It is often the case that a person is unable to recognise the explanation and description of what it means as the whole subject is too painful to acknowledge. To highlight it and face it, is worse than the pain, therefore it remains buried until the time comes to resolve it or the circumstances improve. The saying of "time is a great healer" frequently can be seen creating solutions and making life easier for people and so we see the corresponding changes in their feet.

I remember two occasions when the skin on my own heel cracked. One was when I was going through a time of great life change and I found it hard to remain my normal positive self. I knew that things were going well in the long term, but short term it hurt and I was worried about the effect of it on my family and security. It was of no great shock when my heels suddenly split. I think I even laughed at the observation "how true"! The second time was when my youngest son was leaving home and going to university. I had planned in my own mind how I would deal with it and decided what I would do, and how I would handle it when he went. Even though I had really thought it through very thoroughly and planned lots of great activities, I still missed him and within two days my heels had cracked. Luckily it had healed over quickly however it did prompt me to take good care of myself and acknowledge the change to both of our lives and the effect it was having on mine. Mind you it did make me laugh again as the best laid plans still did not stop me feeling it.

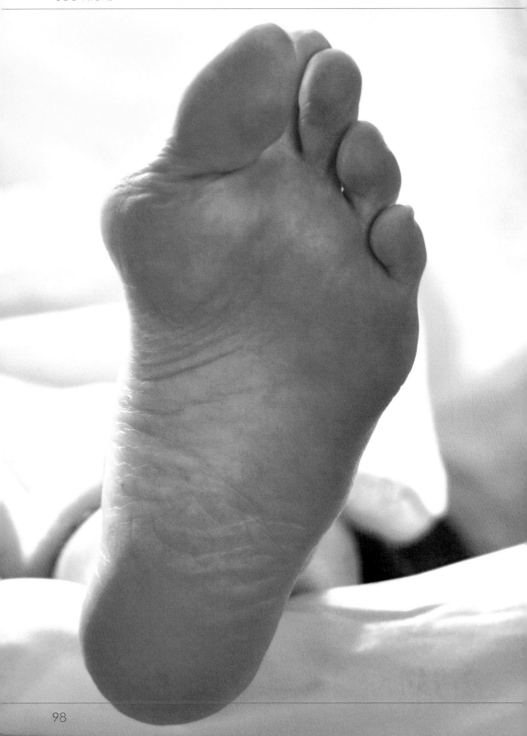

Bunions

A bunion can be found on either foot and may be mild or severe. Some bunions alter the shape and position (direction) of the big toe (Hallux) and some just protrude from the base of the big toe.

Bunions are found at the feeling level (horizontally) and the thought region (vertically).

Bunions are a reflection of the need to create personal space and a need to be acknowledged. They are pushing out into extra space. Some bunions are very painful, and some are mercifully painless.

A bunion may appear red or white in colour.

Example:

Red = angry or embarrassed.

"I have wonderful children and a loving partner and all I could wish for. I love looking after them but I am still feeling unfulfilled. What's wrong with me?"

or

"Why do I do everything to get it all done and yet still have no time for me? I am always working"

White = Exhausted or drained.

"I am exhausted doing everything to keep everyone going and together."

or

"I am running out of energy but still need to keep going, they rely on me."

The actual bunion can be linked to the big toe as well as the 'thoughts' issues of the big toe. The thoughts area is on the big toe and the next area down around the bunion is at the 'feelings' level. This is when the person is not living the life that would be right for them and not honouring who they are and how they live.

When the bunion causes swelling and the bone to grow out, it is as if the person is saying "give me some space".

I once watched a TV programme where a lady was going into hospital to have her bunions 'done'. She was pestering the consultant to get the operation over with as soon as possible to allow her to get back to her family so that she could carry on where she had left off. This is a classic case where the bunion is likely to come back as she was carrying on in the same way as before.

The alternative would be to let her family take the strain for a while. Encourage her to put her feet up and let them do the jobs for once and take care of her. That way they may appreciate what she did more; they may notice what it takes to run the home and care for the family and also how much she achieved. They may also enjoy being given some power of their own and letting her rest. She may notice that they are more capable than she thought they were and realise that she can change and let go of the reins a bit. If 'Mum' always does it then they have no room to step forward and achieve for themselves.

Bunion on right foot – This happens when the person is striving for space on what they do and how they feel accepted by the male expectations of life.

Bunion on left foot – This occurs when the person is struggling to cope with the demands on them and needing space for themselves and their feelings. This is often associated with nurturing and over nurturing or over giving and is linked to the female pressures, expectations and ways of life.

Bunions on both feet – This appears when the person feels pressure or lack of space for themselves in all areas, what they do, how they give time and their energy to others.

Many people say, believe or worry that bunions are hereditary as maybe their grandparents had bunions and now the person's mother has them too. The logical progress of this thought and reality is to assume that their children will too. This is understandable as bunions are a physical condition and they are appearing in successive generations. However, it may be the ways of life and living patterns that have been handed down instead that are causing the bunions. It could be a combination of factors, however once an individual finds peace in being themselves and allowing other people to be okay with that (or not), then their bunions reduce and even disappear.

The key is the change in attitude and beliefs and that is not an easy thing to achieve. Altering a whole family's doctrine of "how one lives life" is tough and may be too much to manage. However if people find ways of being able to have their own space, be the real person that they are and conform, or not conform, then the pressure goes and their feet can rebalance.

Swollen Feet – Oedema

Any swelling relates to lots of withheld emotion and unshed tears. This can be a wide range of emotions and the very nature of the swollen feet or ankles could be because the person does not want anyone to know that they are feeling emotional about something and are burying their feelings. This could be fear and wanting to look confident, it could be resentment and feeling that they should be able to cope or wanting to do or be better at whatever life they are living.

This is always a tricky subject as the nature of the problem is almost always subconscious. Since they are not consciously aware of the issue and have decided to be happy or confident or think that "this is just the way it is", all this emotion (feeling) is kept inside.

- Filled with emotion
- Need to release limitations
- Essential to get into own flow
- Earth bound and forgetting life purpose
- Emotions are weighty
- Energy pooling and not flowing

Explanation:

Water = fluid

In so many cultures the analogy of water is used to represent emotion.

Emotion = energy in motion = "e" motion.

The question is 'what is the type of energy and what is the motion?'

Lots of energy or feeling = lots of emotion,
Small amount of energy or feeling = less emotion.

The more water or fluid that is in the legs or ankles, the more stuck or stagnant the person is feeling. Stagnant water is always a problem, whether it is in a pond, a lake or your body as water needs to flow to be vibrant and healthy energy.

No flow = stagnation.

Water is processed in our bodies via the kidneys where it is filtered for excretion or retained for use within the body. In orthodox medicine this health problem relates to heart or kidney problems.

In Chinese medicine the kidneys are the 'house of fear' and this may explain why when we are frightened we need to rush to the toilet! Kidneys are all about the correct fluid balance and when they are under stress they are alerting us to the fact that our lives are out of balance and there may be fear to overcome. Or perhaps there may be too much work or pressure within family, home or work. Balance is what we are aiming for and when this is addressed the equilibrium is restored and water (and energy) will flow freely.

Remember that the person may not be consciously aware of it as it is buried in their ankles – as far away as they can get it! It could be a feeling that they have to conform to what society or family expect "I am expected to", as opposed to " I want to or choose to".

Still water runs deep = fluid retention. This is a 'deep' issue that the person is quite likely to be unaware of and possibly reject anyway because they need their coping strategy to work. They may have a coping strategy of smiling, being helpful and looking calm and serene on the outside whilst worrying like mad on the inside.

If the fluid retention is in both legs or ankles then the problem may be across the board. When the problem is on one side and not the other then this issue may be as follows:

Swollen right leg = worry of things to do, male attitudes, how a male views you or brought you up, worries about actions required that affect the family (outside of ankles = family and security, horizontally and vertically).

Left leg = self nurturing or care worries. Looking after family or their confidence in ability to look after others or mother's attitude to things and beliefs.

The resolution is to be more loving to self (love = heart) enjoying what they are doing. Gentle movement to reduce stagnation and rest with enjoyment of life.

"If you like or love it - do it more. If you don't like it do it less!"

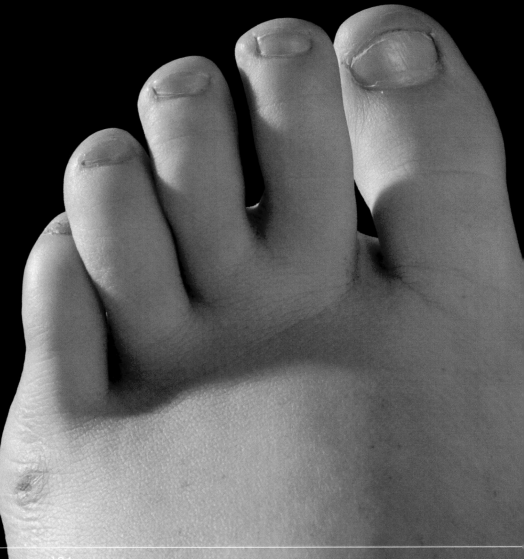

Toe Reading

The toes represent thoughts and the person's thinking. There is a difference between thoughts and thinking. Thinking is an active process whereas a thought can be something that just passes through. Generally, thinking takes some time and a thought is more transitory.

When we see someone's toes we can get a sense of their comfort or discomfort with their thoughts about a wide range of things according to which toe it is that is out of alignment, damaged, high in colour etc.

Foot and toe reading can help practitioners and therapists to decide how to approach people and situations during a clinic session. If you can see on their feet that they are already overwhelmed and in 'overload' it is good to acknowledge, rather than suggest they take action and do something about it. When someone is overwhelmed, the last thing they need is another list of actions to take. When you have assisted the client to feel better (as seen on their feet) you may then be able to offer advice and tips at a later date.

Personally it is good to notice any bumps, bruises, cuts, blisters etc on your own toes or fingers. It can help you keep on top of issues in your own life and take action if necessary. If you notice that your fingers or toes are improving in appearance this is a great validation that you are doing well in life.

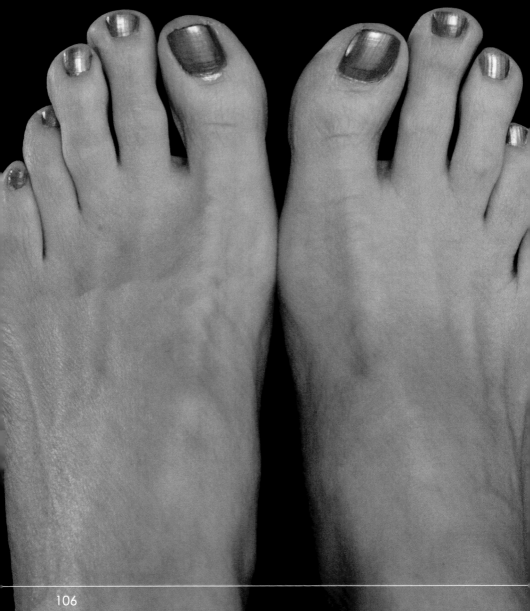

Toes

Straight Toes

If toes are pointing straight ahead then this means that you are living your own life, following the appropriate way of living for you. You are on track.

The straighter your toes, the better it is for you as this indicates you are on your own path of life and honouring yourself and hopefully others too.

Crossed Toes

When toes are crossed over, i.e. one toe is laying across or over another toe, then this means that you are following someone else's track. It could be what is expected in your family, your upbringing, social conditioning or feeling that this is the way you 'should be'. It is often linked to being 'well behaved and well brought up' or doing as you are or *were* told. Whenever you see crossed toes, it indicates that there is room for more discovery of self.

The toe that is the most visible from the plantar (sole) view is the dominating theme. Sometimes one toe 'overwhelms' another. The most common toe to be squeezed out is the second (feeling) toe. This means that the person hides their feelings and is frequently linked to thought processes such as:

"I don't have feelings – they are difficult, embarrassing and get me into trouble, I don't know how to handle them so I don't have them."

Crossed toes that have good movement and flexibility indicate the mentally flexibility and agility required to make life changes.

Crossed or bunched toes that are rigid mean that the person has developed coping and safety strategies that do not allow room for flexibility. In this instance, the person may feel like 'this is just the way it is' and has 'locked down' their way of living and will probably continue to behave, respond and react in the same way. As a consequence, their lives, feet and toes will not change either.

Toes with movement = thoughts can move or change.

Toes with no movement or rigid = rigid outlook on life and no room to manoeuvre.

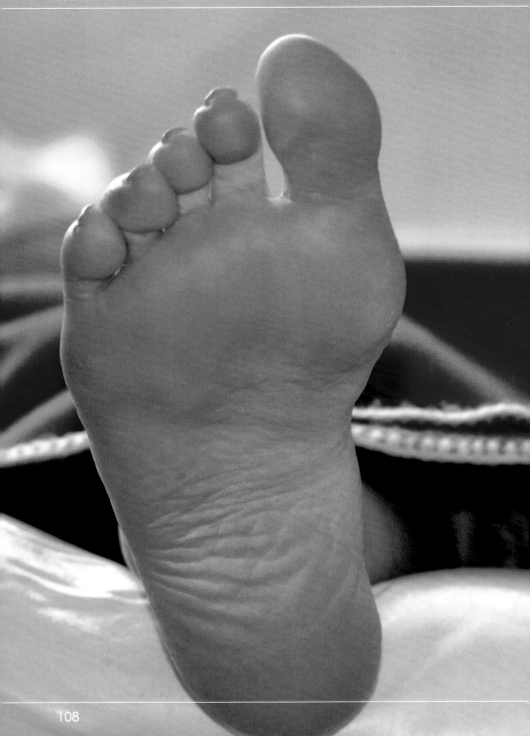

Length of Toes

The natural curved shape of the foot is due to the reducing length of toes from big toe all the way down to the little one. Generally the big toe is the longest and the little toe the shortest. This can vary however according to individuals. Everyone's feet are different and reflect the different aspects of a person's personality and gifts.

Look at the overview of the foot and the significance is in the length of the toe as opposed to the normal range. Some toes are more noticeably longer than others and some are shorter than normal.

Prominent Toes – Noticeably Longer

The longest or most predominant toe is the area that you or the person has the most natural talent and gifts in.

Shorter Toes

The shortest or most hidden toe is the one that the person feels the most uncomfortable in. The shortness can be due to a number of factors. It is important to take into account if the toe appears to be short when in actual fact it is bent over or curled. If you imagine the toe to be gently straightened out, it could then become a considerably longer toe, indicating the person's true capabilities within the particular aspect of life.

Short toes are an indication of where the person has more limited capabilities and can frequently be balanced by other longer toes (where their natural capabilities lie).

Full toes mean full thoughts = may be too many.

Empty toes (squashy and depleted) = no energy left for thoughts and the activity of thinking.

Large, Long, Wide Big Toe (Hallux)

The bigger the toe is, the bigger the capacity of the 'theme' of the toe. The big toe is about thinking and thoughts.

The length of the toe is an indication of the person's capacity to think into the future and the way ahead.

A Head = Using their head to think or have thoughts that can project forwards.

A long thin big toe – Relates to a single minded ability to plan, think and recognise the implications for the future on a subject. The person can be said to be 'clever'.

A wide big toe – Shows the person's capacity to think and recognise the implications on a wide range of issues and subjects. This person is said to be 'wise'.

A long and wide big toe – Indicates a clever and wise soul who is great at knowing the wider implications of thoughts, action and issues. Often said to be an 'old soul' and wise beyond their years.

This can be seen even in babies' toes. A baby born with a really big toe is certainly an evolved soul who will be very 'knowing'. They may be both wise and yet challenging especially when questioning some of the madness of the world, its structure and routines that may now be outdated.

A person who has a wide big toe is able to pay attention to their thoughts.

A person with a long big toe is good at thinking.

Think and thoughts are slightly different.

- **Thoughts** are more passive and come and go. They are our connection to our inner self, intuition and subconscious. Thoughts can bring startling revelations, great awareness and 'knowing'.

- **Thinking** is an active process that we are taught at school and are encouraged to do. It is a conscious process that involves brain activity.

Someone with a wide, big toe can get a sense of an imbalance or incongruence and then set about finding out what it is and what to do about it.

They initially get a thought that "something is wrong here", then set about tracking it to develop their awareness of where the 'problem' lies in order to resolve it.

Others may view people as intense as the person with a wide, big toe want answers. Also, they do not understand that this type of person is hyper aware and also keenly sensitive.

A person with a wide, short, stumpy big toe uses withdrawal as a coping strategy, whereas a person with a medium length, big toe will be very aware and then kick in with their analytical (and process driven) thinking to find solutions.

Someone with wide, long big toes is very aware and skilled at thinking of ways to move forward to resolve issues. This is because they get the wider implications.

People with wide big toes are often misunderstood individuals. They are often misunderstood as they have a wider view on life and see beyond the obvious. Some people like to be fixed on one point and yet a person with a broad big toe may be challenging to them as they see other aspects of life.

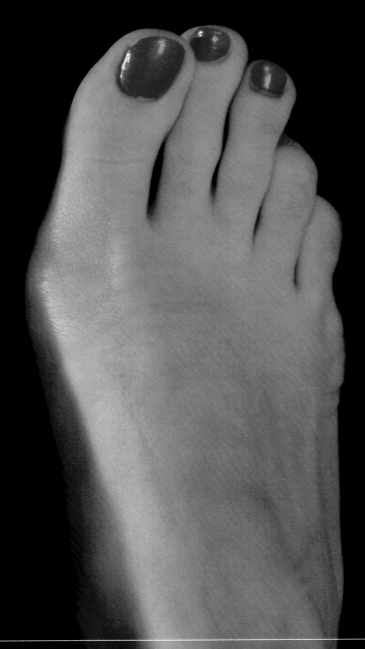

In contrast, someone with a slimmer big toe may find that any subtle clues or imbalances just floats by and they never pick up that there is an anomaly or incongruence in a situation or circumstance. They will be highly involved in thinking about the present and the future and making a difference.

In an argument:

- A person with a wide big toe is more emotional and sees the wider picture, other views or alternative approaches

- A person with a long big toe is more rational, has a more clearly defined (linear) approach

- Wide toe = wide view

- Thin toe = single minded

- An oil and water situation!

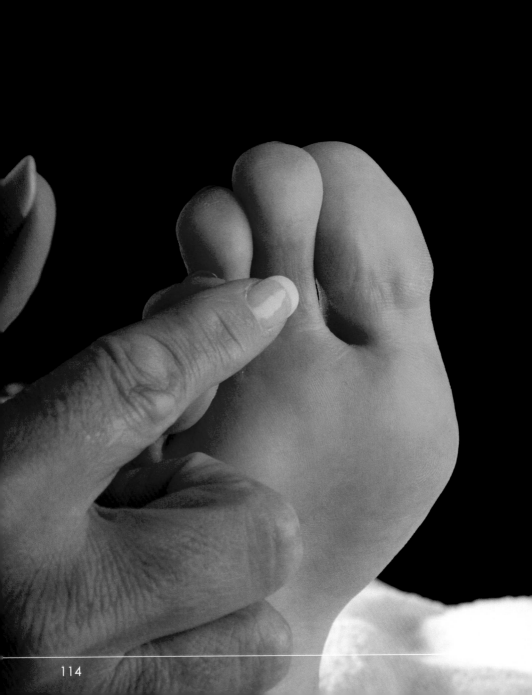

Longer Second Toe

A second toe that is longer than the toe either side, is sometimes called Morton's toe. It is thought that about 10% of the population have a longer second toe. If this toe is very long it can feel painful as it can end up taking the pressure that would normally have been taken by the big toe. This extra length means that feelings are predominant in this person's life and they are led by their feelings.

Anyone with a longer second toe is quite intuitive. They just 'know' things but may not know how they know!

The second toe relates to thoughts (horizontally) and feelings (vertically) and, if it is especially long, indicates that they have a great capacity to feel, sense and be aware. They have intuitive thoughts as opposed to doing endless thinking.

Longer Third Toe

When someone has a longer third toe this indicates their creative abilities and capacity to get things done. Many people talk about doing things but do not actually get things done. Whereas, anyone with a longer third toe has great strengths in getting things done,

If they also have a good length feeling toe, they will be a great person to work with, have on a committee and a great friend who can make things happen whilst respecting the feelings of others.

If, however the third toe is long but the second toe is quite short then this person is not so aware of the feelings of others. This can create problems as the individual blindly gets things done and takes action with little or no awareness of the impact that this is having on others. This is especially true if the second toe on the left foot is short as the left foot is more about others.

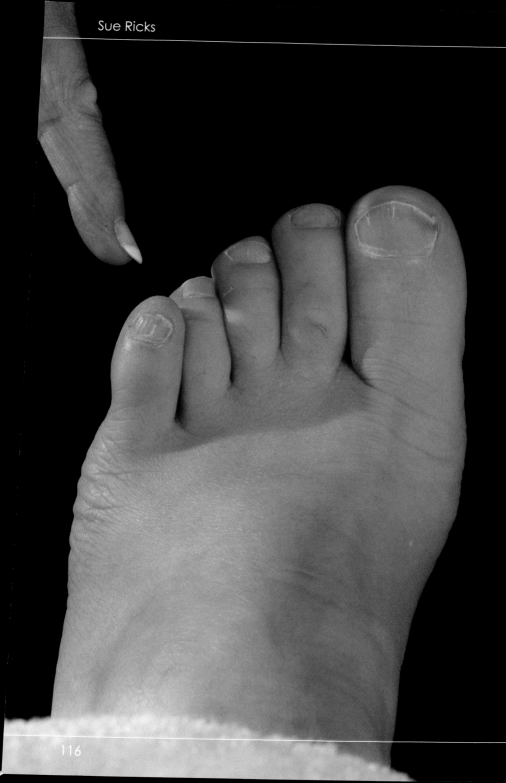

Long Fourth Toe

When the fourth toe seems to be longer than normal, this indicates that the person has good communication abilities. This means they can speak about current and future times plus communicate effectively about what lies ahead.

Communication comes in many ways:

- Speaking

- Writing

- Demonstrating

- Body Language

- 'Communications careers'

Long Fifth (Little) Toe

A long fifth (little) toe is not seen that often and shows that the person knows their own strengths, their individual way forward and does not feel the need for approval from family, friends or society. They may have their own way of doing things and frequently do things that are more unusual. They find their own life path.

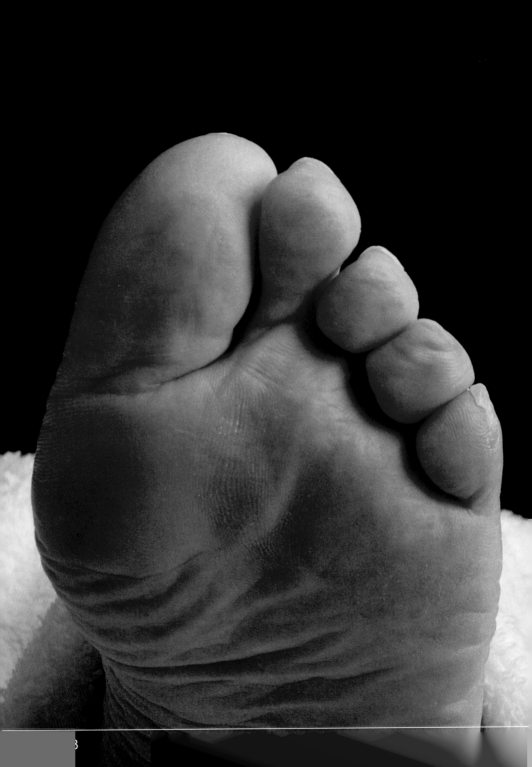

Little Toe

The little toe is sometimes called the "confidence toe". It relates to how we think about our family and security issues. If we feel secure and are happy with how we fit in the family and are thinking good and positive thoughts about them then our confidence and self esteem are assured.

However if someone is feeling or thinking any of the following:

- I don't fit in

- I don't belong here

- I am different

- I am not accepted

- I am not acceptable as I am

- I am supposed to operate differently

- I am supposed to think differently

- I am anxious around my family

- Other people are better than me

Then it is possible that their little toe will be small and pinched and may be pushed / leaning towards the next toe. A very confident self assured person who knows their own mind and totally trusts themselves will have an upright full and straight little toe.

Little toe with 'sharp faces'– see photo
This means that they have two opposing views on whatever the 'theme' of the toe is.

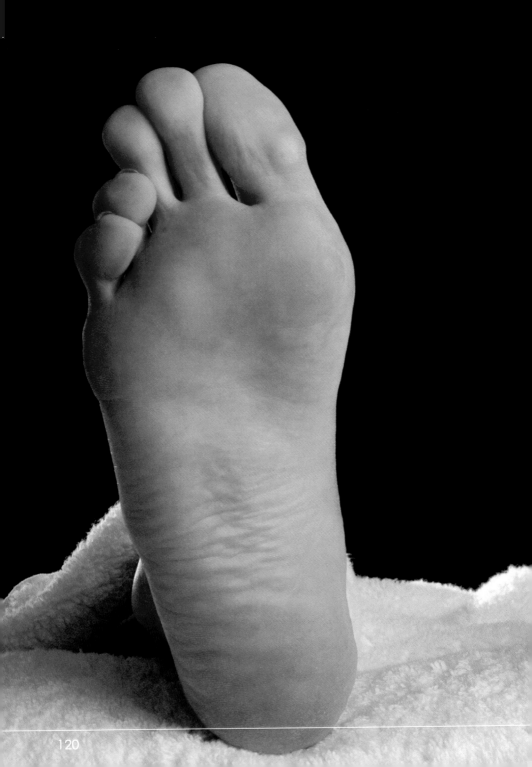

Example:

Two clearly defined 'sides / faces' to the little toe.

This toe relates to thoughts (horizontally) and family & security (vertically), therefore someone may adore their children (one view) but be thinking *"if they leave their toys in this mess one more time; I'll ....!"* (second view)

or

I love my Mother and will do anything for her (view one) but be thinking *"please do not ask me to go to the shops again, we've just been!"*

Interestingly enough I have found that many people who appear supremely confident actually have small or misshapen little toes! This is because they have had to work incredibly hard to cover up and over compensate for their feelings of inadequacy or lack of confidence.

Some time ago I treated an extremely muscular, toned and athletic gentleman. He had all the appearances of success and high self esteem. He was well dressed, spoke confidently about his work in body building, he even arrived in the latest Porsche. During the initial consultation he detailed his skeletal problem that had occurred as a result of his body building. When I looked at his feet he had both red and white patches all over his feet (red equals anger and embarrassment and white equals washed out and exhausted). He had a large big toe that relates to his generous capacity to think but his big toe was also slightly raised (pulled back) indicating that he was keeping his thoughts very much to himself. His little toe was virtually nonexistent, it was tiny, almost shrivelled and pushed hard towards the fourth toe so deeply pinched with almost two clear 'faces'.

Whenever you find the little toe with two sides (faces) on the plantar (sole) aspect of the toe, this is an indication that the person has two entirely different views / thoughts about their family "I really love my family / mother / brother etc" or "they are driving me nuts". It is common and normal to have conflicting views and yet the more extreme they are the more it shows in the feet. Some people even have a piece of hard skin that is almost razor sharp on the little toe. This is an indication of very separate and opposing views about their family and security issues.

Long Toe Stems

It is good to notice the length of the person's toes as this tells you how expressive they are. Pay attention to which toe is the longest (feelings, communications etc). The person will have a better ability to express anything that relates to the toe with the longest stem.

Below are the meanings of specific long toe stems:

- 1st (Big/Hallux) Thoughts toe stem - connects thoughts to feelings.

- 2nd, Feeling toe stem – they can express their feelings and let others know how they feel, either verbally, through actions or body language.

- 3rd, Creativity & doings toe stem – they can express themselves creatively through words and creative projects (e.g. music, arts design etc).

- 4th, Communication toe stem – they can speak out and express themselves verbally and also with gesticulations and facial expressions.

- 5th (little), Family & security toe stem – they are very family minded and expressive with, via and through their immediate or wider family.

Wide – Strong Toes

The width of the toes is worth noting as it shows the width and breadth of their appreciation of the toes' theme.

For example:

Wide 1st toe (big) – able to think in many different directions and on many subjects.

Wide 2nd toe (feelings toe) – can appreciate and be aware of a wide range of emotions and feelings.

Wide 3rd toe – able to get things done on a wide range of topics and subjects, e.g. they have a multi creative approach.

Wide 4th toe – can communicate on many different levels and with self and others at the same time.

Wide 5th (little) toe – able to be there for self and family. They have multi connections and think about connecting to family and the wider family (groups, society etc.) in many different ways.

Long and Wide Toes

Anyone with a long and wide toe or toes, has special talents and abilities that are their natural born gifts. It is essential that their life, work and contributions reflect the skills and innate abilities that they have.

When the way of living and working reflects their essential essences as shown by the length and width of their toes, then there will be peace and harmony. If, however, there is a distortion and the person is following a way of life or working that does not honour their natural essence, their true self is compromised and real unhappiness can be the result.

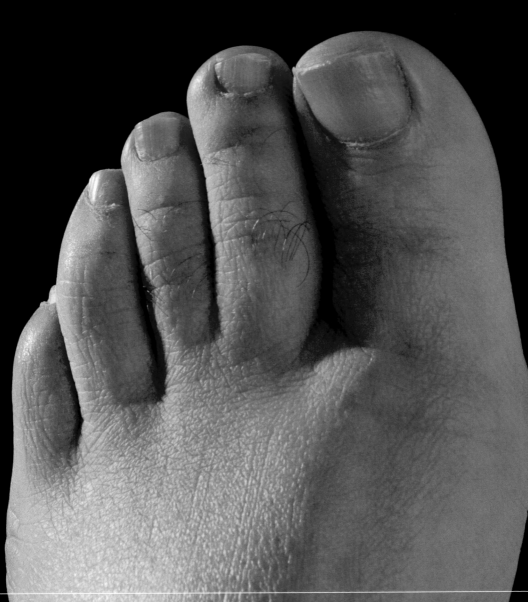

Nails

Nails are your protection and they represent how you protect yourself with your thoughts. Strong nails means that you have strong protective thought patterns that keep you safe. Soft and weak nails represent a weakness in your self-protection systems. Nails become strong and thicker as life becomes healthier and safer.

Ingrowing Toe Nails

The nail is ideally a protection but in the case of an ingrowing toe nail, the nail grows into the toe (usually 1st / big toe). When someone has in growing toe nails, it means the thoughts they are having that they believe to be protecting them (nails) are actually not doing this and are really hurting them, (ingrowing thoughts). In growing toe nails are a sign of mental unrest on issues with what is really helping and what is not.

We all pick up ideas, concepts and thoughts from our family, peers and those around us and build up our own ways of being. Many of these patterns of thought or behaviour stem from well-meaning persons in our past and involve some levels of pressure on how to behave, think or act. I suggest that these pressures can be called "shoulds" and a useful way of seeing how they impact on our lives is to say that our 'shoulds' can become like a disease and be called 'shoulditis'(an inflammatory condition).

Ingrowing toes nails often happen at difficult times in our lives when we are thinking about some difficulties / tough times. If the thoughts we are thinking involve "shoulds", we may believe they are helping us when in fact they are not.

Nail = protection
Ingrowing nail = protective layer / nail is hurting you!
Big toes = thought , therefore the nail is actually hurting you and not protecting you at all.

No Nails

No nail = no protection and therefore vulnerable

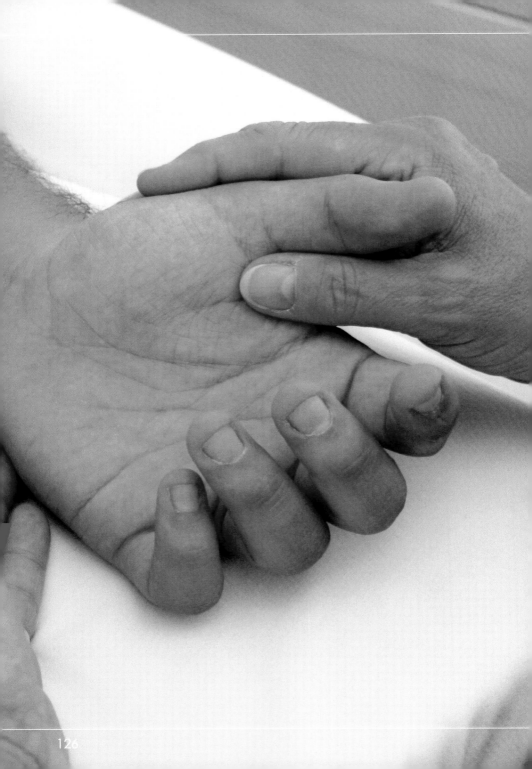

Nail Fungal Infections

Nail fungal infection = infected thoughts. So it's likely to be ideas picked up during up-bringing or being offered by well-meaning family and friends.

I had a particular problem in my teens with my toe nails and I remember several people telling me how I should think. "You need to think about it like this", luckily I have formulated a more appropriate way of noticing my own thoughts now. My nails are now happy, healthy and strong.

Finger Nail Biting

Bitten nails – people bite their nails when they are 'biting' at their thoughts about how to protect themselves. Somewhere deep inside they may have built a plan of how to keep themselves safe and protect themselves then find that this doesn't entirely work. That leaves them feeling vulnerable and so they bite the nail (protection) which leads to the fingers being over exposed (as the nails are not there).

Nail biting often happens when someone has been following the handed down thought patterns and behaviours that impact on all areas of life.

Example:

An overly helpful parent who knows that "they're right" tells a child how to think, act and behave. The child accepts this and thinks and acts accordingly. As the child grows up they begin to realise that these inherited patterns and ways of living do not suit them, as they are not exactly the same as their parents.

It is not until the child breaks out of the patterns that do not suit them and finds their own way, their own strength and confidence to be themselves that the nail biting ceases. The child / adult will only grow strong nails when they have found their own ways of protecting themselves which may be very different to their parent(s).

Review
Benefiting Everyone

Self Care

Remember to take a glance at your own feet from time to time and get a glimpse of what they tell you. You could be smiling, however underneath your feet will tell you how you are really doing.

Once you know your own feet, you may find that you can spot areas in your own life that you wish to enhance, change, address or accept.

One of the participants at a Foot Reading Workshop in the States wrote to thank me for the information she had gained during the training. She said it had been a revelation to her. She had heard others say she had issues she was not addressing but thought they were wrong. She said that she thought she was over everything from her past and nothing was affecting her.

After the class she assessed her own feet and realised she was still very angry with her family and was generally having lots of angry thoughts. She realised that maybe she was being very defensive and causing some of the continuing trauma she saw as 'their' problem. A quick look at her feet revealed that she wanted to address her high levels of emotion and anger. By the time she sent me her email she had already made an appointment to see someone who could help her.

What to Say and What Not to Say

If someone is protecting themselves by covering up a part of their personality or the way in which they are experiencing a life situation, then it is highly irresponsible for anyone to blurt it out to anyone who may be listening. They may not even wish to acknowledge it, even to themselves, so voicing anything can be unacceptable.

Equally if we start to worry about anything then the chances are that we will inadvertently use the laws of attraction and make whatever we are worrying about more likely to happen. If we say something like "wow, you are feeling fed up today", then the person may go away and really dwell on all the reasons why they may be fed up. They may focus on all the things that may be causing them to be fed up and all they think about is negative and constricting thoughts. This can be disastrous and can cause even bigger problems. In foot reading we have a responsibility to the care and attention of the person and remain mindful of the effect that our words may be having. Always highlight their positive qualities.

One student came on the course to learn about reading the feet as she had experienced a bad encounter with a person who had previously read her feet. She had been told that she was not a confident person and was not good at expressing her emotions and that was affecting her health. She then spent the following two years believing that and worrying about it. She developed lots of reasons to confirm this belief too.

On the course she was able to see why she had been told that but what she had not heard (or been told) was that she had the capacity to be a really confident and self assured person. Had she concentrated on the potential rather than the message of permanent failure she had heard, who knows what would have happened. Luckily she has used her bad experience to become one of the most attentive foot readers that I have met. She is very aware of what she says and how the impact of her words can seriously affect others. Her cloud had a silver lining!

A little bit of knowledge can be a dangerous thing! Sometimes it is much better to say nothing than to risk saying something that is accurate, but limiting and can result in deflating a person. What we focus on is what we get more of. When we see something it is essential that this information is presented in a helpful, positive and progressive way, rather than causing someone to feel ever more depressed, saddened or hopeless. There is so much positivity that can be expressed via the reading of the feet or hands whilst maintaining honesty.

Sometimes the saying "if in doubt say nought", may be more appropriate and safer.

Remember that jokes or phrases like: "I did not mean it, I was just joking", can be equally damaging. Spoken words cannot be retracted and the emotional impact may go deep even though the person joins in with the laughter.

If you are not sure then I suggest you say nothing at all until you have had time to think it through.

If you are asked directly and are unsure how to proceed, there are a couple of good options. Sometimes it is all too easy to feel that an answer is needed immediately, and it is often too easy to say something that turns out to be inappropriate when feeling rushed. Firstly, a quick reply saying that you will think about it and let them know later may be more appropriate. Alternatively, just pause, wait, check your response (in your head) and then reply. It may seem like ages in your mind but it is worth it in response to a person and the effect it might have on someone's life.

Be kind and generous towards others and all opportunities.

Good friends of mine live by the motto "kindness and patience". I love this way of living and love them too!

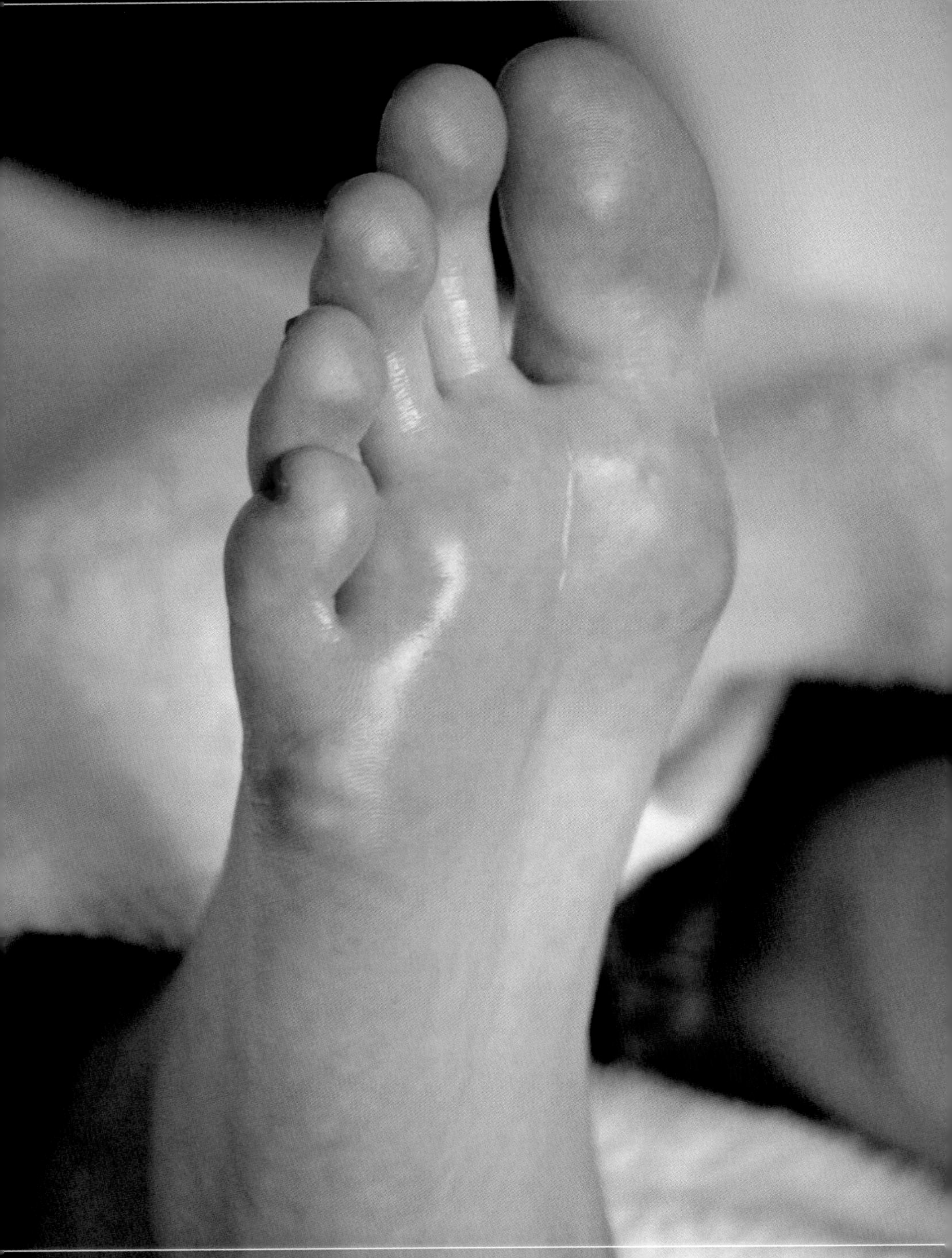

Self Reflection

This is a useful reference for you when finding out how you personally are coping, and if things are going as well for you as you believe.

Many years ago I was feeling that I was managing my life and responsibilities as a mum of two great boys, our home, my practice and training school quite well. It was only when I was on holiday that I noticed I had developed a hard layer of yellow skin over the balls of my feet (especially my left foot). My feet alerted me to the fact that I was actually feeling quite fed up and protective of my feelings. It also showed me that this feeling of being fed up was through quite a few areas of my life.

Explanation:

Yellow = fed up
Balls of the feet = feelings (horizontally - all areas) creativity and doing, communication, family and security (vertically)

Hard layer of skin = protection

All of this was quite relevant because even though I was pleased with the way I was doing and managing things, I was still feeling fed up due to a big change in my personal circumstances that affected both my children and myself. I had thought things were going okay, but my feet helped me to see what I needed to do next to acknowledge and address my feelings. Acknowledgement is often the key to change.

Luckily, thanks to my continuing passion for personal development, Gentle Touch™ Reflexology and working with gifted practitioners, I worked through my issues and those previous areas are now fine. Even my feet agree!

This Book

This book is simply what is seen on feet and hands and what it means to me. I hope you have found it useful too! I conclude this book with some more examples of what I see on feet with a few pointers to a range of things visible to use, see and recognise. Enjoy!

My intention is to share my love and passion of this subject and it's impossible to get this in just one book! I have therefore made this book, Fantastic Feet, to provide everything useful to get you started and develop your knowledge.

The second book will provide a great deal more detail and further in-depth learning opportunities.

Foot reading is a massive subject, the more you understand the deeper and wider the subject becomes.

The next book goes into foot and hand readings' connections to:

- Reflex points (as used in Reflexology)

- The significance and meaning of numerious factors including corns, hammertoes and peeling skin etc.

- Energy and chakra connections

- Metaphysical meanings behind various organs and areas of the body

- Bringing it all together

The more we know and understand, the more we can support and assist.

Graze / Communication
Area (Double)

Graze indicating
struggling about
communication relating
to what they are handling
and how to take care
of themselves.

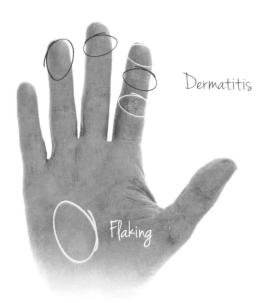

Dermatitis

Flaking

Contact dermatitis with
areas of redness
(anger / embarrassment)
and exhaustion/lack
of energy.

Flaking, peeling skin =
irritation and revealing
new self.

See next book
for more detail.

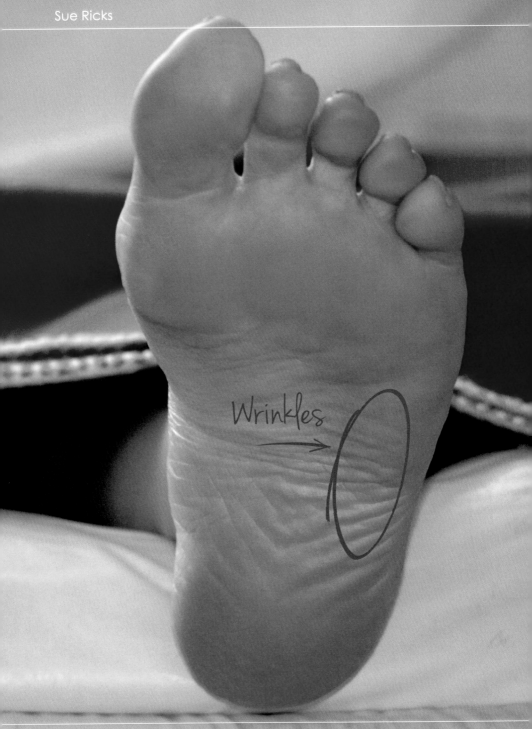

Wrinkles

Grid Example

This image (left) shows the area that relates to how someone is communicating and the energy involved. Here the area is especially wrinkled and shows the effort that they are putting into communicating. They are drained of the emotional effort going in to communicating, making the skin shrink and appear wrinkled.

Communication is a very broad subject that relates to:

- Internal or external communication
- Verbal and non-verbal communication
- Communication with yourself and / or with others

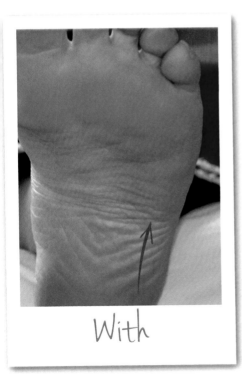

With

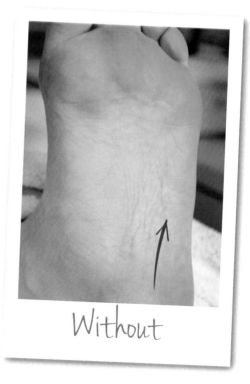

Without

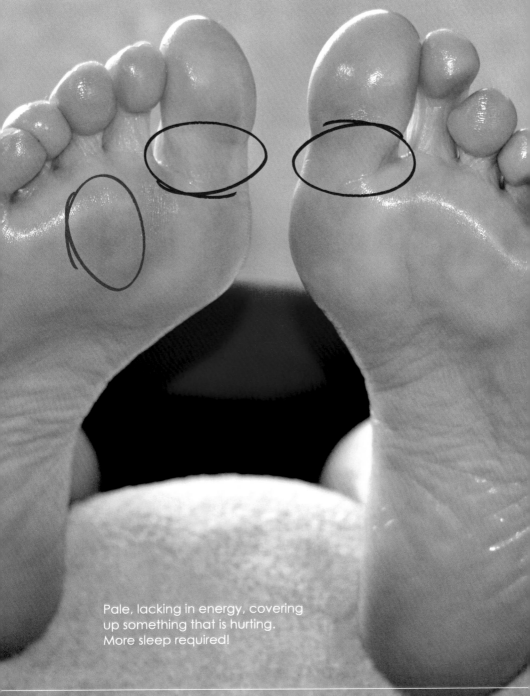

Pale, lacking in energy, covering
up something that is hurting.
More sleep required!

A Carer's Feet

An over-giver –
broad foot. Being
swayed by other
people's opinions,
struggling to find
their own way.

Hidden Feelings

Could be
a good
communicator
but does not
speak out

Lacking
confidence

Wishing for
personal space
subconsciously

Shouldering
too many
responsibilities
that make
them fed up

Foot Reading Chart

GENTLE TOUCH ™
REFLEXOLOGY ®

Family & Security
Communication
Creativity & Doing
Feelings
Thoughts

Thoughts
Feelings
Creativity & Doing
Communication
Family & Security

Thoughts

Feelings

Creativity & Doing

Communications

Family & Security

suericks.com

Hand Reading Chart

GENTLE TOUCH ™
REFLEXOLOGY ®

Left hand (upper):
- Family & Security
- Communication
- Creativity & Doing
- Feelings
- Thoughts

Right hand (upper):
- Thoughts
- Feelings
- Creativity & Doing
- Communication
- Family & Security

Lower hands:
- Thoughts
- Feelings
- Creativity & Doing
- Communications
- Family & Security

suericks.com

Foot Reading
Meanings Grid

Thoughts

Feelings

Creativity & Doing

Communications

Family & Security

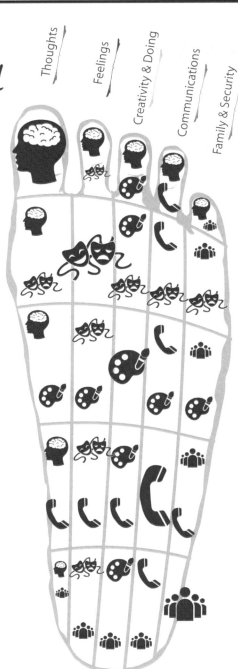

www.suericks.com

Index

A

Active   81
Actor and the actress   17
Adulthood   63, 83
All ages   73
Angled feet   88, 89
Angry / anger   16, 17, 19, 53, 54, 55, 76, 77, 129, 135,
Anxiety or trauma   18
Arch   35, 87
Artistic   85
Attentive foot readers   130

B

Baby, Babies and Children   110, 141
Balanced   13
Ball of foot   35, 57, 87
Bankruptcy   63
Bare feet   22
Base of foot   87
Battered   69
Beach   22
Beauty salons   22
Big feet   83
Big toe   16, 27, 29, 122
Black   53, 62, 63, 74
Bleeding   95
Blood   97
Blue   53, 60, 61, 77, 74
Blushing   55
Body language   47, 117
Bone deformities   12
Both feet falling in   89
Both feet turned out   89
Boundaries   92
Broad   86, 87
Brown   53, 63, 65, 78,
Browned off   53, 65
Bruised emotions   53, 69
Bunions   99, 101

C

Calm   17
Carer's feet   139
Careers   13, 117
Change of circumstances   18
Chatterbox   47
Chi   97
Child   63, 69, 73, 95, 59, 127
Chinese binding   85
Chinese medicine   103
Church   47
Clever   110
Cold   94
Colour/s   41, 12, 18, 41, 49 - 78
Communication   27, 31 - 37, 41, 46, 61, 117, 137
Community   47
Confetti   50
Confidence   16, 27, 35, 35, 41, 47, 95,
Control   92
Coping strategies   13
Cracked   16, 95 - 97
Creativity   27, 33, 41, 46, 117
Crisis   87
Crossed toes   107
Current situation   61
Cuts and bruises   9

D

Dance classes   22
Deep breathing   76
Deep inside the foot   75
Deeper emotions   65
Deeper the issue   75
Dependable and reliable   87
Dependence   47
Depth of colour   75
Dermatitis   135
Diaphragm line   33
Doing   27, 33, 46, 81
Dominant   81
Dorsal aspect   39
Double sectors   40 - 45, 95
Dr William Fitzgerald   25
Dual theme   42, 43 - 45

E

Earlier trauma   63
Early childhood   61
Embarrassed   53, 54, 55
Emotion   76, 102
Emotional pain   95
Empty   53, 109
Empty toes   109
Energy   8, 46, 71, 102, 103
Exhausted   53, 70, 71
Expressive   122

F

Family   19, 26, 27, 33 - 37, 41, 47, 87, 91, 107, 117, 119
Fear of dying   63
Fed up   53, 56, 57, 65
Feelings   27 - 37, 41, 43, 46, 107, 115, 117
Feet   75, 87
Feet defects   12
Females   81
Feminine   81
Finger nail biting   127
Fingers   37, 105
First toe   76
Five (little toe)   29
Flaking   135
Flat footed   90
Floppy feet   91
Fluid retention   103
Foot dorsal grids   45
Foot plantar grids   45
Foot positions   12
Foot reading in action   18
Fourth (ring) finger   31
Fourth toe   29
Frustrated or annoyed   53, 58, 59
Fund raising   87
Fungal infections   127

G

Gentle Touch Reflexology   16, 133, 141
Glossy magazines   22
Grass   50, 67
Green   53, 66, 67
Gym and fitness studios   21, 22

H

Habitual way of thinking   67
Hallux   25, 27, 29, 122
Hand grids
Hand palmar grids   44
Hand sector   43
Handle life   10
Hands   31
Hand Reflexology   48
Happy   53, 72, 73
Hard skin   41
Head   110
Health challenges   63
Healthy   53, 72, 73
Heart   97, 103
Heel   35, 95
Heel of your hand   37
Hereditary   101
Horizontal grid   32, 33, 36, 38
Hospital   19
Hot   94
Housebound   65
Hue   50, 61, 63
Hurt   53, 61, 63

I

In growing toe nails   125
Independence   47
Index finger   31
Initial observation   16
Intention   21
Internal or external communication   137
Internal tension   92
Intuitive   115

J

Jealousy or envy   50, 53, 67

K

Kidneys   103

L

Lacking energy   70
Language   47
Large toe   41
Large wide feet   82
Layers of skin   74
Left foot   81, 89
Left leg   103
Life style   67
Lines and marks   12
Little finger   31
Long / longer   110, 117, 122, 123
Long big toe   110
Long fifth (little) toe   117
Long fourth toe   117
Long thin big toe   110
Long toe stems   122
Longer second toe   115
Longer third toe   115
Loss of blood   95
Love   18, 97, 103

M

Males   81
Martial arts studies   22
Masculine   81
Meanings of colours   7
Memories   63
Memory   69
Mid arch   67
Middle finger   31
Middle toe   65
Mirror   14
Morton's toe   115
Mother   71, 103

N

Nails   125, 127
Narrow feet   84, 85
Natural   13, 18, 53, 72, 73
New direction   10
Non-verbal   137
Nurse   19
Nurturing   81

O

Oedema   102
On track   107
Orange   52, 53, 58, 59, 74, 77, 78
Overwhelmed   105

P

Parent or carer   6, 95
Partner   6
Passive   81
Patients   19
Pelvic girdle   33
Permission   21
Personal development   18
Personal information   15
Personal power   91
Personality traits   13
Photograph   15, 16, 22
Pink   53, 73
Plantar aspect   38
Positive qualities   130
Potential   13, 83
Practitioners and therapists   105
Privacy and disclosure   21
Prominent toes   109
Protecting   57
Protection   133
Purple   52, 53, 68, 69

R

Rapport   22
Rational   113
Recliner chair   17
Red   16, 53 - 55, 76, 77, 78, 99, 135
Reflexology   92
Reframe   76
Rejected   61
Relaxation classes   22
Repeated colours   75
Resentment   65
Right foot   81
Right foot falling in   89
Right foot turned out   89
Rigid   92, 107

S

Sadness   60
Sandals   22
Scarlett   55
Scars   12
Second toe   29, 43
Security   26 - 28, 31, 33, 34, 36, 95, 103, 117
Self   8, 14, 18, 55, 77, 81, 129
Sense of loss   63
Shape   12, 15
Shoes   8, 17, 22
Shorter toes   109
Shoulder girdle   33
Size of feet   12, 83
Skin cracks   95
Skin infections   12
Small feet   85
Social networks   47
Sock fluff   41, 75
Sole   21
Soles facing each other   90
Soles of the feet   18
Speaking   117
Speech   47
Spot colour   65, 75
Stagnation   102, 103
State of mind   9
Straight toes   16, 107
Strength   8, 13
Stress   18, 46
Subconscious   21, 102
Subtle or significant changes   10, 15
Subtle shade / tone   50
Success Tips   141
Surface   74, 75
Swelling   41
Swimming pools   22
Swollen feet   102
Swollen right leg   103

T

Temper   55
Temperature   94
Thin toe   113
Thinking   111
Third toe   29
Thoughts   27 - 37, 33, 40, 41, 46, 105, 109, 111, 115, 117
Three Steps To Enjoying Life   141
Thumb   31
Ticklish feet   93
Tip toes   90
Tiredness   70
Toe positions   12, 15
Toe reading   105
Toes   35, 47, 75, 76, 105, 119 , 122
Top of foot   87

U

University   97
Upset   69

V

Verbal   137
Vertical grid   24, 31, 38
Vitality   71

W

Waist line   33
Walking on the outside of their feet   91
Washed out   53, 71
Water   102
We stand up to life   10
Weakness   8
White   52, 70, 71, 94, 99
Whole foot   87
Wide   87, 110, 113, 119 ,123
Wise   110
Withdrawn   53, 71
Within layers   74, 75
Wrinkles   136
Wrist   37
Writing   47, 117

Y

Yang   81
Yellow   53, 56, 57, 78, 133
Yin   81
Yoga   21, 22

Z

Zones   25

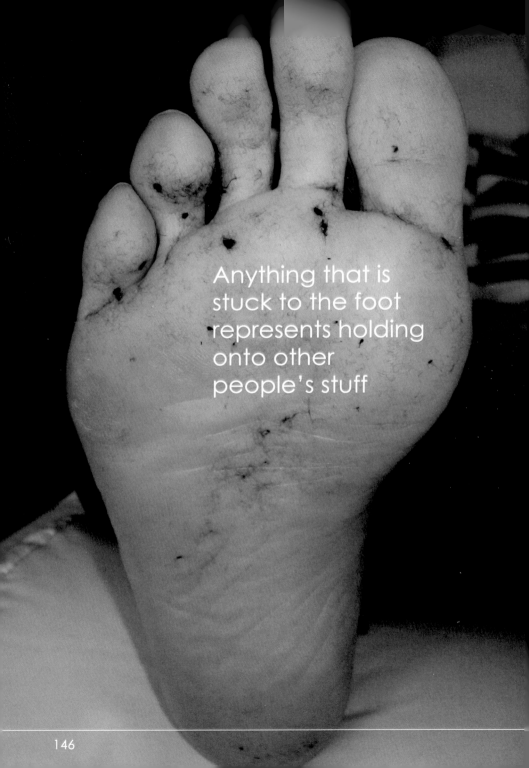

Anything that is stuck to the foot represents holding onto other people's stuff